# HERBAL
# PLANTS

# HERBAL
# PLANTS

## HISTORY AND USES

# MARK EVANS

## STUDIO EDITIONS
### LONDON

## PUBLISHER'S NOTE

This book is not intended for prescribing medicines for curing afflictions. Its purpose is not to replace the services of a physician but rather to serve as a reference source on medicinal plants. We emphasize that the use of any of the information in this book for purposes of self-treatment without consulting a physician can be dangerous.

*Herbal Plants: History and Uses*
published in 1991 by Studio Editions Ltd.
Princess House, 50 Eastcastle Street
London W1N 7AP, England

Printed and bound in Czechoslovakia

ISBN 1 85170 778 6

# Contents

latini coriandrū Egiptii
oscū Omnib' notū frigide
uirtutis ēe. ad lubricos.

herba coriandrū coq̃t ad ter
as inoleo & incapud mittat.
coriandri seminis g̃na xi aut ad mu ẽe uci to
xiii inlinteolo mundo detela pari
alligato puer aut puella uirgo at
ad femur sinistrū ppe inquẽ te
neat. ꞇmox ut pael' fuerit pari
remediū cito soluat ne itestina
soluant. ad frigora. ad cottidianas. ad quartanas.
herbā coriandu ubi mane undis ad olitorem ppo
situ accedis ad eū ꞇpicies dena riū ꞇ tolles fasci
culū de coriandro ſ; ñnomina & portab tecū usq: dum hora
suspecta ueniat. cū aū illa t̃sierit & nich ꞇ prouenirit subse
picis illū p̃te dū ãbulas & noli p̃te respice liba vit te
ad pulices. porcilaca.

Herbe coriandri aq̃ in
domo spargr. A g̃ci
andragne. Theonina.
Pphe themaaros. Daci Lax.
latini Porcilaca. Portastrū.
Porcilaca nota ē ōmb; frigide uirtu adan g̃ nit ñmiū
tis atq: redarguentis ēe. erba por ſflu uiū.
tilaca sṛta bene fac & pse ꞇcū oricard
mirabis effectum. ad stomachi infla tio né.
herba porcilaca p̃gat & ĩ aceto sumpta
ĩtre iflationē tollit.

# Introduction

Herbs have been an integral part of our history since the dawn of time, and throughout the ages they have been highly prized and cultivated for their properties. Every chapter of history carries stories of how plants have been of value, and this is very much still true today. As increasing numbers of species are fast disappearing, we are recognizing what a tremendous potential store of medicine, food, etc., the plant kingdom holds.

It is perhaps useful at this stage to say what is meant by a herb, since the narrow definition used by botanists to denote flowering, non-woody plants is of little value when looking at society's use of plants. To a herbalist, a herb is any plant, or vegetable matter, that can be useful medicinally. Plants have, of course, been used for many other purposes as well, such as food, clothing, shelter, the source of dyes, and so on, but this is a good working definition. In this book we shall look mostly at the healing properties of herbs, though some of their other uses will also feature.

As well as the history and origins of the uses of herbs, and some of the beliefs that have grown up around them, some details of their appearance and tips on cultivation will be of help to those who wish to grow herbs themselves. This is an increasingly popular area of gardening, for herbs have so much to offer, as attractive, often highly aromatic plants in their own right and as the source of flavour in food or possibly first-aid remedies in the home.

Obviously, herbal medicine is a detailed and complex subject and there is no substitute for consulting a qualified medical herbalist. The final area that is covered in this book is a review of modern medical uses of herbs by professional herbalists. This gives some idea of the range of problems that can be treated with herbal medicine, and of the help that plants can give.

The World Health Organization estimates that 85% of the world's population relies most heavily on traditional, herbal medicine, making it several times more widespread than conventional Western medicine. Even in the latter, some 15% of doctors' prescriptions are still plant-based. With our present concerns for ecology and the environment, herbalism seems set to be the model for the medicine of the future, as well as the source of our good health over the last few thousand years.

*Glycyrrhiza glabra*

Published by Dr Woodville Oct:1. 1792.

# CHAPTER I

# The History of Herbs in Society

The history of herbs is essentially the history of mankind itself, for every culture and civilization has used herbal plants extensively throughout recorded time, and, it would seem, back into pre-history.

Probably our earliest introduction to how much our forebears used herbal plants can be found in the oldest archaeological remains of early man, in caves situated in part of what is now Iraq. Pollen grains found in association with human bones show that a wide number of plants were used in some way by our remotest ancestors. Those same plants still grow in the region, and recorded medicinal uses of them right down until today would indicate that they may well have been important for healing for Neanderthal man too, some 60,000 years ago.

Another clue to what may have happened in the past can be gained by looking at certain tribes today, in South America for example. Here we find that each tribe has an extensive knowledge of local flora, cultivating its own 'medicine garden' for use in illness. Studying their practices has more than an anthropological interest; it can often reveal new information on the medicinal powers of herbs which is of value to us all.

Such people seem to have an almost instinctive awareness of which plants to choose, an ability which is found in many wild animals and even in some ways in cats and dogs. If this is a faculty which we once had, then we have lost it over the intervening millennia; how many people would know which plants to pick for a natural remedy if they were ill?

When we come to recorded history we soon find references to herbs in all the great civilizations of the past. One of the oldest systems of medicine, that established in China, has kept herbal records from the very beginning; written in around 2800 BC, the work known as *Pen Ts'ao* lists over 300 herbal medicines. Many of these still play a major part in Chinese herbalism to this day. The ways in which the old herbalists practised, their formulae and indications for use have been a constant feature over all this time.

People visiting a hospital in China and opting for traditional, herbal medicines will be given a prescription to take to the herbal pharmacy. The diagnosis and prescription follows guidelines that have been laid down for centuries; thus the herbal treatment is a living testimony to the ancient past, as well as an effective form of medication for the Chinese. The 'barefoot doctors' encouraged by the late Chairman Mao continued this direct link to the rural areas.

Moving westwards, the equally ancient culture of India also has a thriving herbal tradition. Over many centuries the ancient Vedic manuscripts were written, giving advice and rules on all aspects of human life, including medicine. The system of Ayur-Vedic medicine that is widely practised in India, and indeed by a few people in this country, has been passed down since then. There are many similarities between the Chinese, Indian, Abyssinian and ancient Egyptian systems of medicine, showing that there must have been a good deal of interchange amongst these peoples.

From fabled Babylon we have lists of medicinal drugs, or *materia medica*, re-

Common Liquorice from Gerard's *Herball*, 1636.

Opposite: Liquorice *Glycyrrhiza glabra* from Woodville's *Medical Botany*, 1790. Liquorice is an ancient flavouring and medicine. Grown in England since the sixteenth century and listed in all pharmacopoeias in one form or another. One of the most popular cough remedies, it has soothing, anti-inflammatory and healing properties, among others, and is highly regarded by herbalists.

45

Caraway *Carum carui* from Woodville's *Medical Botany*, 1790.

substances have been regarded by some medical historians as evidence of the purely magical nature of medicine at the time, rather than being a serious system of physical treatment.

Interestingly, modern research is beginning to show that even these drugs have definite therapeutic properties. Urine from pregnant women, or animals, was used in traditional medicines centuries before hormone replacement therapy came on the horizon. Some of the prescriptions undoubtedly were long and involved peculiar additions in order to imbue the treatment with a magical quality, but this can be seen as simply a way of affecting the attitudes of the patient and treating the whole person, which modern psychotherapy might well endorse.

The medical practitioners of ancient Egypt were often also priests, and treatments involved rituals to purify the patient on a spiritual level as well as medicines for the body. Herbs were used at every stage, from cleansing the altar to being burnt for the purifying, aromatic vapours that they gave off, to the medication itself.

Sometimes herbs had a mind-altering property that was considered a vital part of the healing process. There are echoes of this side of medicine in many other cultures, and the role of the *Shaman*, or witch-doctor, in tribal society included using these powerful herbs to induce a state of trance, either in himself or in the sufferer.

The basic physical effects of the herbs were of much greater concern to the Greeks; whilst they gained a lot of their knowledge from the Egyptians, with the rise of the Hippocratic school from the fifth century BC they emphasized herbalism as a system of medicine, divorcing it from magic and ritual.

Herbs were an integral part of Greek society at this time. As the practitioners evolved into a medical profession, using herbal remedies, advice on exercise and diet, and some hydrotherapy applica-

corded in the reign of King Hammurabi during the eighteenth century BC, whilst the Ebers papyrus found in 1862 near the site of Thebes dates back to around 1500 BC and lists hundreds of herbs. Ancient wall carvings at Karnak depict herbgathering expeditions returning from Syria and other countries. The Phoenicians were famed as sailors and merchants, and they traded in medicinal plants throughout the ancient world.

These records often show the same kinds of plants cropping up all over the Middle East. The Ebers papyrus, for instance, has some 700 plants, many of them, such as caraway, liquorice, squill and linseed, still used by herbalists now. Mingled in with the herbal remedies were some mineral and animal drugs, such as oryx offal, and these stranger

Opposite: Squill from a twelfth-century copy of *Herbarium of Apuleius*. Squill (*Urginea maritima*) is one of the oldest of herbal medicines; one preparation was created by Pythagorus in the sixth century BC. It is a strong expectorant, but larger doses easily irritate the stomach, and it is not often used now.

herba bouis lingua cũ melle & pane pisata uice malagmatis mirifice rumpit. Leges eã mense iulio.

Noĩa herbe scilletici.

Agreci uocat Scinieas. aľ Scilla malcibizon. aľ Pan crocion. aľ typonos. Egiptii Siptu. Pphe Obtalmon. Itali Scilla rubra mascula. aľ Bulbo scillites. ad hidropiciã. Herba scilla bullos torret. deinde cir cũ purgat. & mediũ el maã decoqt. Cũ madidũ fue rit ex imitto & exeo tres obolos da potui cũ melle & aceto euacuat purinã. ad pmones. Herbe scille tici qd e ĩ medio ei cũ oleo deferuefactũ atq; ea qd dolore exhibent puncta sedabunt. ad pa rantia. Herbe scilletici radix pisa ta cũ aceto & pane iposita paranicũ mirifice sanat. ad hidropicos. Herbe scilletici foliũ subiecta sublingua sitĩ cõpescit. Leges eã omnĩ tpe.

Noĩa herbe cotilidon.

Greci cotilidon. aľ cerasafrodites. aľ Phales. aľ Sthicas. aľ Stergeton. Itali Vmbilicũ ueneris. Nascit in tectis aut. ĩ monumĩtis. ad strumas. Herba cotilidon pisata cũ arungia suilla feminis sine sale eqs pondib; calidũ strumas discutit. Leges eã õi hiemis tempe ascit locis solidis & circa uias. ad canis morsus. Herbã gallicrus teres cũ arun gia hamnisith. & pane domestico. & iponas mox sanabis. Idem & duricias discutit. Noĩa herbe Marrubii. Greci Prassion. aľ Epotrion.

Sgilla rubea

Cotill    Cotilidõ

The preparation of a medical potion derived from certain herbs. From Hippocrates: *De Diversis Herbis*. Thirteenth century.

tions, so there also grew up a thriving trade in herbs. These traders, the *rhizotomoki* or 'root-gatherers', collected herbs and sold them to the physicians as well as to the public. People who could not afford the professional doctors' fees often turned to the herbal suppliers for advice as well as for plants, and this is a pattern which we see repeated throughout our history.

As herbalists became more organized so the first herbals, listing the plants and their uses, appear for physician and herb-supplier alike. For instance, in the first century BC the physician to King Mithridates Eupator of Pontus, Crataeus, wrote what was probably the first illustrated herbal. The king himself was an avid herbalist, and is the source of the name for Agrimony (*Agrimonia eupatoria*), a highly popular Greek herb.

For the citizens of ancient Greece and Rome, herbs were an essential part of everyday life. When bathing, they would be anointed or massaged with oils imbued with the aroma of various flowers, a practice taken over from the Egyptians but developed as a fine art by the Romans especially. During their feasts, herbs were lavishly used to flavour the food and wine; they even ate little sweets made from caraway, dill and other seeds to aid their digestion between courses (of which there could be many!). Herbs were burnt during religious ceremonies to cleanse the air and propitiate the gods, and most importantly herbal medicines were the chief source of healing in illness and injury.

Most of the Greek and Roman herbal practitioners were army doctors, for instance Dioscorides, who travelled with Nero's armies across Asia Minor in the first century AD. As the conquering soldiers spread over the then known world, the physicians carried with them seeds and plants for their favoured remedies. By this means they encouraged the rapid spread of herbs into Europe and the Middle East; many of our aromatic plants such as rosemary and lavender probably came here by this method.

As well as their plants, the Greeks and Romans brought with them their more sophisticated ideas on health and healing; whilst there was inevitably some exchange of knowledge about herbs and their uses, we largely took on board the classical view of medicine that these physicians shared. Their ideas were to remain the principle source of knowledge for some 1,500 years.

A fundamental part of their concept of health was that of the four 'humours', representing the essential qualities to be found in man, and giving rise to the four basic temperaments: choleric, phlegmatic, sanguine and melancholic. These were related to the Elements — Fire, Water, Air and Earth respectively — from which all things were believed to be made. The Elements were seen as qualities as much as actual substances, and disease was classified according to the way that the balance between them was disturbed in the individual.

Herbs were also classed according to how they affected the humours, and this idea can be seen in the writings of herbalists right up to Culpeper in the seventeenth century. There are a lot of parallels between the classical notions of hot, dry, wet or cold diseases, and corresponding herbal remedies, and those of Chinese or Indian herbal medicine still alive today. Western herbalists also still find these ideas useful, together with our improved knowledge of how the body works and how herbs affect health.

Following the division and finally the fall of the Roman Empire, much of the old herbal knowledge went eastwards, and the Arabic culture absorbed it for several centuries, before returning with it in the invasions of Spain and southern Europe. They were responsible for one particular development, that of distilling essential oils out of plants.

From the days of the ancient Egyptians, aromatic oils were made by infusing the plant in a vegetable oil; following Avicenna's day, physicians began to extract the essence directly. This laid the foundations both for the perfumery industry in later times and for the widespread interest in aromatherapy and the medicinal use of essential, volatile oils that has developed in the last twenty years or so.

In this country, we were left with a variety of sources of herbal medicine. The monasteries carefully guarded and copied by hand the classical medical texts

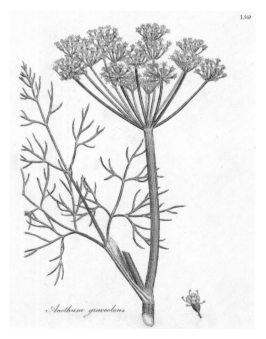

Dill *Anethum graveolens* from Woodville's *Medical Botany*, 1790.

Opposite:
Top: 'The Thebaidi Monks' by Lorenzetti.

Bottom: A detail from 'The Thebaidi Monks' showing the monks tending the vegetables and herbs.

of old. Each monastery kept its 'physic garden', for making remedies to heal the monks and people living nearby. As they explored herbalism over the centuries, the monks developed ways of preserving the medicinal properties of herbs. They can be credited with the making of alcohol extracts, the herbal liqueurs some of which still exist today; Chartreuse, for instance, contains over 140 different herbs. Alcohol-based tinctures are the commonest method of prescribing herbal medicines in modern herbalism, although lacking the flavour of a liqueur!

In the west of England and in Wales, the Druidic culture had remained influential, and the Druids used herbs extensively in their rituals and medicine. Their tradition was an oral one; if you became apprenticed to a Druid you had to learn by heart the names of the plants, and their parts, what they were good for and how to administer them. When the Druid eventually died, your apprenticeship was over and you became the next Druid.

The Druidic system once again intermingled medicine and magic but there were more down-to-earth approaches even in Wales. The Physicians of Myddfai developed a rational form of herbalism during the eighth to the thirteenth centuries that was strongly influenced by Hippocratic writings and ideas.

In rural areas across Britain, folk medicine remained much as it had been in pre-Roman times, herbalists giving remedies on the practical basis of observing that they worked rather than according to the elaborate classifications of Galen. There was a divide between the empirical folk medicine of this kind, often the province of the village wise woman, and the professional physicians of the growing towns, who increasingly turned to more drastic measures to speed up nature's responses.

There is a little evidence of new herbs coming into the green pharmacy of the times during the Anglo-Saxon period, notably in the *Leech Book of Bald*, but it is not until the advent of the printing press that a renaissance in herbalism is seen throughout Europe. Until then, the Myddfai system of health-care, together with a similar approach based on Hippocratic ideals in Salerno in southern Italy,

was the best and soundest approach around, but affected only a small number of people. The Latin and Greek texts were unattainable or unintelligible to the great majority.

When trade and communications with the Arab physicians expanded, Europeans came into contact with the old texts once again and physicians incorporated Arab ideas and herbal medicines. A classic example of this is senna, which was heavily prescribed by Arab doctors to "evacuate excess humours". The contrast between this type of medicine, reliant on large and complex prescriptions, and the gentler style of the herbal healers is striking.

As the development of printing started to bring the ancient medical texts to a wider readership, so more people came to be interested in medicine in all sorts of ways. There were the physicians, mostly giving herbal remedies, but gradually incorporating the new mineral-based medicine that was developing. As mentioned, they looked to compound prescriptions, often violently purging their patients, or else bleeding them (not for nothing were they called 'leeches'!).

Their training was almost entirely theoretical, involving study of the classics as well as medical books for as many as fourteen years at Oxford or Cambridge, and in later times often finished with a 'Grand Tour' of Europe's finest cities. They prescribed on the basis of the Galenical theories, without really establishing whether the remedies actually worked in practice. Indeed, few of them actually troubled to learn about plants at all, and were heavily criticized for this by those who did.

Another grouping were the barber-surgeons, who would shave you, bleed you or cut off a leg, depending on what was required! Many of them had an active interest in herbal prescriptions as well, but eventually they evolved into quite specialized professions.

For most people, especially the poorer folk, the apothecaries or herb-suppliers were the main source of advice as well as medicine. It is this group that carried on the practical herbalism of the past, and are the forerunners of today's herbal practitioners. Interestingly, as they became more organized and highly trained

in the eighteenth and nineteenth centuries, the apothecaries developed into what is now the general practitioner, while some retailers, like Jesse Boot, became the High Street chemists.

In the countryside, the village wise woman, or perhaps the lady of the manor, continued to provide simple remedies for all kinds of ailments, on the basis of seeing what worked. This tradition, mostly an oral one passed down to daughters and grand-daughters, is another source of useful information that has been largely ignored.

Herbs were used in medieval times in almost every sphere of human activity. Aromatic plants such as meadowsweet, sweet woodruff or mint were strewn on the floors of chambers, oils and unguents were rubbed into the skin for scent, people carried pomanders and posies to cut out the stench of the streets. Food was given strong colour and flavour by

Meadowsweet from *Commentarii in Sex Libros Pedacii Dioscoridis* by Pierandrea Matthioli, 1565. Its old Latin name Spiraea was the origin of the word aspirin; unlike the drug it is very useful in gastric inflammation and excess acidity. An important medicinal herb today, as it has been over many centuries.

Opposite: A fifteenth-century miniature of a medieval town garden from *Le Livre de Rustican*.

Pl 45

the liberal use of herbs, local ones like parsley and marigolds for most people and fiendishly expensive exotic spices such as cloves, saffron and nutmeg for the wealthy.

Medicine was the main use for herbs, although people did not necessarily separate food from medicine: garlic, sage, thyme and other antiseptic herbs would be used in cooking with meats to avoid potentially fatal food-poisoning as much as for their flavour.

With all this interest, people started to write new herbals, and the fifteenth, sixteenth and seventeenth centuries saw the great flowering of writing on herbs, both in Latin and increasingly in the vernacular. These herbals, like the Greek ones before them, were partly descriptive of the hundreds of herbal plants then in use and partly an explanation of the 'virtues' or medicinal properties of the herbs.

With the writings came botanical illustrations. In some cases these were rehashed from ancient pictures, and bore little or no resemblance to the real plant; but where the artist and author were really interested in nature they de-

Woodruff from Gerard's *Herball*, 1636.

Tobacco from Mrs Loudon's *The Ladies' Flower-Garden of Ornamental Annuals*, 1840. 1. *Nicotiana tabacum* 2. *N. acuminata* 3. *N. noctiflora* 4. *N. multivalvis* 5. *N. longiflora* 6. *N. glutinosa* 7. *N. persica* 8. *N. langadorfii*. Tobacco (*Nicotiana tabacum*) was occasionally used in the past as a relaxant, for example in asthma, but the toxic effects of nicotine etc. have been increasingly apparent for years. Even when introduced by Sir Walter Raleigh in 1586 it was violently opposed, as a 'noxious habit'.

veloped the art to a fine degree, often rivalling in beauty and accuracy the work of Victorian botanists.

In Tudor times, the power and prestige of the physicians led to them asserting their authority over the surgeons, who often gave medicine as well; they in turn denounced the barbers for carrying out surgery, and all occasionally attacked the apothecaries for prescribing remedies. This led to a series of Acts of Parliament, which created more and more restrictions on who could practise what kind of medicine, particularly in and around the rapidly expanding London area.

This reached such a pitch that eventually Henry VIII and Parliament passed what has sometimes been called the 'Quack's Charter', allowing herbalists "having knowledge and experience of the nature of Herbs, Roots and Waters" to practise legally. This has been one of the mainstays of our freedom to get herbal treatment ever since.

The King himself was an avid amateur

Poppies from Mrs Loudon's *The Ladies' Flower-Garden of Ornamental Annuals*, 1840. 1. *Papaver horridum* 2. *P. setigerum* 3. *P. nudicaule* 4. *P. somniferum* 5. *P. rhoeas* 6. *P. persicum*. Opium Poppy (*Papaver somniferum*) has been used since ancient times as a medicine to sedate, and relieve pain sensations. Its hypnotic and addictive properties make it of course illegal nowadays outside conventional medicine.

herbalist, making medications and ointments for himself and others, and this shows that herbs were an essential part of life for all members of Tudor society. Queen Elizabeth I continued her father's practices, often dabbling in herbal preparations.

The seventeenth century continued to see herbalism flourish, with the publishing of more herbals, especially that of Culpeper. For the physicians, however, there were beginning to be debates and arguments about whether to include the newfangled chemical and mineral medicines. These were highlighted by a court case in Exeter in 1604 between a physician, Dr Woolton, who belonged firmly to the old tradition, and Thomas Edwards, an apothecary who was successfully selling mercury and the like as well as herbal remedies.

Edwards sued for libel, and won the case. The new medicines won too, having been popularized by Paracelsus some sixty years before. Paracelsus himself was mainly a herbal practitioner, something which has been conveniently forgotten by medical historians, but he used these mineral, toxic medicines for the fatally dangerous infectious diseases of the day that were otherwise not dealt with.

By the eighteenth century this chemical approach had won the day, as far as the regular physicians were concerned. Professional medicine reached a pretty low state, with blood-letting and mercurial concoctions the chief mainstay. Many apothecaries flourished by providing these heroic medicines, often at great profit.

The poorer and more rural people continued to use the cheaper and safer herbal medicines, and to grow their own domestic remedies, but herbs declined in numbers in prescriptions. They were still

Jalap (*Ipomaea purga*) from *Curtis's Botanical Magazine*. A Mexican member of the bindweed family, Jalap is a strong purgative. It is made from the roots, which are rich in an acrid resin, and was used most in the days of 'brisk medicine', when purging was considered essential to treatment.

17

given, but some of the newer, more dangerous ones were preferred for their quick effects, such as opium, senna and jalap — purging was a popular therapy.

By the time Queen Victoria came to the throne, such treatments had reduced the health and vitality of people, especially women, to a weak state. There are many references in works of the Victorian era to the pale languor of gentlewomen, and this was not only due to frequent childbirth. This led to a resurgence of herbalism, as new ideas and remedies from America mingled with native herbal medicine to offer a serious rival to the dangerous practices of the physicians.

In America, the Pilgrim Fathers had discovered that the Indians were essentially a hardy, healthy race. Their system of healing was based on exercise, a simple diet, a kind of hydrotherapy in the 'sweat-lodges', and herbs. This has much in common with the Hippocratic approach, with a history stretching back into the mists of time.

Many of the settlers learnt from the

Yellow Violets from Gerard's *Herball*, 1636.

Indians, and went about selling or prescribing herbal remedies to the homesteaders. They came to be termed 'White Indian' healers, and were an influential force in the frontier regions. It is the Indian tradition that lay behind the development in the early nineteenth century of a revived botanic medicine. The catalyst for this was Samuel Thomson, whose methods were immensely popular in America, with agents throughout the country dispensing his advice and treatments.

Thomsonian ideas were brought to this country and found a ready audience, notably in the less wealthy areas of the Midlands and northern England. Herbal suppliers and practitioners grew in numbers again. In the countryside, the old skills of making home remedies from the garden and hedgerows still persisted, but access in the towns was more restricted, and apothecaries were a major source of supply.

By the 1850s the 'irregular' physicians were organizing themselves, linking together American and traditional British herbalism, and in 1864 the National Association of Medical Herbalists was established. This later became the National Institute of Medical Herbalists, and to this day this is the foremost professional body of hebal practitioners; indeed, it is the oldest such body in the world.

Herbs were used in other ways too; the Victorians delighted in flowers for their own sake, and perfumes were nearly all made from aromatic plants. The favourite was violets, and everyone from the Queen down wore them or used their perfume. The great variety of herbs that were put into foods in the Tudor days had gone, but some continued to be valued.

By the end of the nineteenth century, however, herbal medicine was no longer a major force, although cherished by those that did use it. Partly this was because the conventional medicine had become less dangerous, with a decline in the use of the highly toxic chemicals or bleeding. Partly, too, it was due to the increasing prosperity that the Industrial Revolution was bringing; people could now afford to turn to the new, attractively packaged patent medicines that

were being offered. Former herbal apothecaries such as Jesse Boot realized that there was more money in such products, and 'Boots the Chemist' was born.

During the early years of this century, the National Institute of Medical Herbalists (NIMH) and other organizations were constantly involved in battles to retain people's right to choose herbal medicine. Prejudice, ignorance, professional jealousy and money seem to have been the driving forces behind many of the attacks that came herbalism's way. One of the main sources of help for the beleaguered herbalists was massive public support, and this shows the depth of feeling there still was for herbs, even if they were much less widely used than in earlier centuries.

Since the 1970s, herbs have become much more fashionable and popular again. Their benefits in cooking are now much appreciated, a visit to a garden centre or major show like Chelsea gives dramatic evidence of their popularity in gardening, and herb teas are on sale in every health shop, and even in some supermarkets.

As people have become more disenchanted with conventional medicine, its impersonal approach and the side-effects of its drugs, so the interest in herbs for healing has blossomed. The over-the-counter sale of herbal remedies has grown steadily in the last 20 years, and on the Continent especially is big business. In Britain, the professional medical herbalist has never died out and today the National Institute of Medical Herbalists has nearly 300 Members. Whilst not at the peak level of the Middle Ages, the interest in and use of herbs in society is now on a definite upward path.

Opposite: Mandrake from Mrs Loudon's *The Ladies' Flower-Garden of Ornamental Perennials* Vol II, 1843–44. 1. *Mandragora autumnalis* 2. *Solanum etuberosum* 3. *Physalis viscosa*.

# CHAPTER II

# *The Great Herbalists*

The development of herbal medicine over the last two thousand years or so has been marked by the contributions of great historical figures. As knowledge about health, disease and the body has increased, so the ideas concerning treatment have been modified, but a good deal of our practical information about the uses of herbs can still be seen in the writings of major herbalists from the past. One of the pleasures of modern research into pharmacology is how often the traditional applications of herbal medicines as noted by these old practitioners can be confirmed.

Probably the first major figure, with an influence on approaches to health and healing that is still relevant today, is Hippocrates (468–377 BC). He lived in the great era of ancient Greece, when tremendous advances were being made in culture, philosophy and the development of rational thought. It is virtually impossible to establish which, if any, of the so-called Hippocratic writings were actually by the man himself, but the concepts that have been attributed to him were to dominate the best medical centres for many centuries after.

The Greek and Roman figures who stand out were often those who wrote widely about botany and natural history in general, such as Theophrastus and Pliny. The latter was a prodigious writer, and his enormous tome on natural history suggested that there was a herbal remedy for every disease, if we could but find it.

Opposite: Herbs being dug up and made into medicines under the direction of a sage. From a twelfth-century copy of *Herbarium of Apuleius*.

One of the most important of these works was compiled in the first century AD by the army doctor, Dioscorides. He had travelled widely with the armies of Nero, and his work *De Materia Medica* was the prototype herbal pharmacopoeia. Such was the quality of his writings that in the sixteenth century Gerard was still quoting extensively from it.

Perhaps unfortunately, the character who became the model for the majority of medical practitioners, including the medieval physicians, was not Hippocrates but Galen (131–200 AD). Galen was a surgeon to the gladiators of ancient Rome, and eventually became physician to the Emperor Marcus Aurelius and his successors.

Galen refined the ideas of the humours into an elaborate and complex system that laid down a rigid framework into which medicine had to squeeze with increasing difficulty for around 1,500 years. His long and successful career seems to have made Galen a rather pompous person, absolutely confident in his own opinions and inflexible in his views — possibly he would have made a successful consultant physician today!

Apart from his completely theoretical approach to medicine, which was to be the guiding principle for generations of doctors, as opposed to the empirical stance of the herbalist healers, Galen was influential in advocating vastly expensive, complex medicines rather than single herbs. Official (herbal) medicine was therefore made up of long mixtures of remedies for a problem, determined by the humoral imbalances that the patient suffered.

Several centuries later, the Arab physician Ibn Said, better known as Avicenna (980–1037), extended Galen's ideas in his vast work *The Canon of Medicine*. This tied up the knowledge of disease and herbal medicines with astrology, creating an intricate pattern of diagnosis and prescription that made argument or disagreement very difficult. From these two sources, the typical medieval physician

The naturalist surrounded by plants. From an illuminated page of Hippocrates: *De Diversis Herbis*. Thirteenth century.

A Dutch formal garden. Among other plants that can be identified are tulips, irises, crocuses and daffodils. From *Hortus Floridus*, Crispin de Pass 1614.

was trained in a highly theoretical way to have an answer for everything; he was known as a 'mouthing-doctor', while a surgeon was a 'wound-doctor'.

Herbalism itself has few major characters to highlight its path from the end of the Roman Empire. The Anglo-Saxon work of Bald and the approach of the Physicians of Myddfai demonstrate that a more practical, rational herbal medicine was still thriving, but it is not until the aftermath of the Black Death, and the rampaging spread of syphilis over a century later, that we find the explosion of new herbals and the renaissance of the great herbalists.

England, in fact, had always been at the vanguard of the movement to create new or modern-language herbals, a process that had been encouraged by King Alfred some few centuries earlier. Copies of older texts, such as the fifth-century Herbarium of Apuleius Platonicus, were given additions, notes and even illustrations by keen herbal users.

In the sixteenth century we again find a number of important figures and authors of herbals. Many doctors of this time did not even know about the plants that were available for medicines, and the few who did were scathing in their condemnation of their colleagues' lack of interest and practical knowledge. The German physician Leonhart Fuchs, after whom the fuchsia is named, was one such, as was Dr William Turner (1520–1568). The latter's *Herbal* of 1551 used Fuchs's woodcuts for many of his illustrations.

Some other herbalists of significance throughout Europe at this time were Gesner in Germany, Matthiolus in Italy and the Dutchman Dodoens. This last writer had his works translated into English by Henry Lyte, and a later version was the foundation for the writings of Gerard.

In many respects, the greatest of these Tudor figures was John Gerard (1545–1611). Certainly his *Herbal*, first published in 1597, has remained the most popular such work of his time, and in various versions is still in print today.

What makes Gerard such a popular figure? Not his medical authority and learning, for much of his information was gleaned or actually copied from other

Herbs being weighed out under the direction of a sage. From a twelfth-century copy of *Herbarium of Apuleius.*

However, his chief employment was as gardener to Lord Burleigh, one of the wealthiest and most powerful men in the land. It is recorded that he grew over 1,000 herbs in these gardens, and they were admired by royalty and nobility across Europe.

The pleasure that comes from reading Gerard's herbal is in the delightful descriptions and stories of the plants that he gives, drawing on his own long experience of their habits and growth as well as their usefulness. Nowadays he would be a famous plantsman or garden designer; he travelled widely through many countries seeking new herbs to grow, and a good friend was Jean Robin, the Keeper of the King's garden in Paris. In his day, growing herbs and using them medicinally were interlinked occupations, and so his talents were divided between both areas.

Following Gerard, one of the most important herbals was written by the London apothecary John Parkinson. In 1629 he published his *Paradisi in Sole* (literal meaning 'park in sun'), and this was a great success. However, the most famous name in the legacy of the herbalists of the sixteenth and seventeenth centuries was one of the last writers, Nicholas Culpeper (1616–1654).

At the time, England under the Stuarts was short of doctors, and the members of the exclusive, wealthy College of Physicians did all they could to keep their knowledge of the old Greek and Roman medical texts to themselves. Most people turned to apothecaries and herbalists for advice and treatment. Culpeper himself started to train as a physician at Cambridge University, but after several years in classical studies he fell in love and decided to elope.

On their way to meet each other, however, his intended bride was killed by a bolt of lightning. Culpeper took this as a message, and turned his back on the restricted world of the physician. He became apprenticed to an apothecary, and then set up his own apothecary practice in Spitalfields, a decaying part of London. He gave advice and herbal remedies to all and sundry, often not charging a fee.

Culpeper was furious at the monopoly of knowledge that the physicians so

writers. This was a common practice in his day; for instance, a good deal of Shakespeare's material is derived from other stories, although transformed by his playwright's skills. Gerard was indeed a practitioner, rising to the eventual post of Master of the Barber-Surgeons' Company, although he seems to have been known as an 'herbarist' first and foremost. His descriptions of the virtues of the plants are most illuminating when he gives personal examples and opinions of their uses, but this is not enough to make his work so enduring. The best version of his work is the 1633 edition by Thomas Johnson, with hundreds of corrections and amendments.

Gerard's prime love, and it would seem his major occupation, was the growing of plants. For many years he lived in Holborn, and grew a tremendously wide range of herbs there.

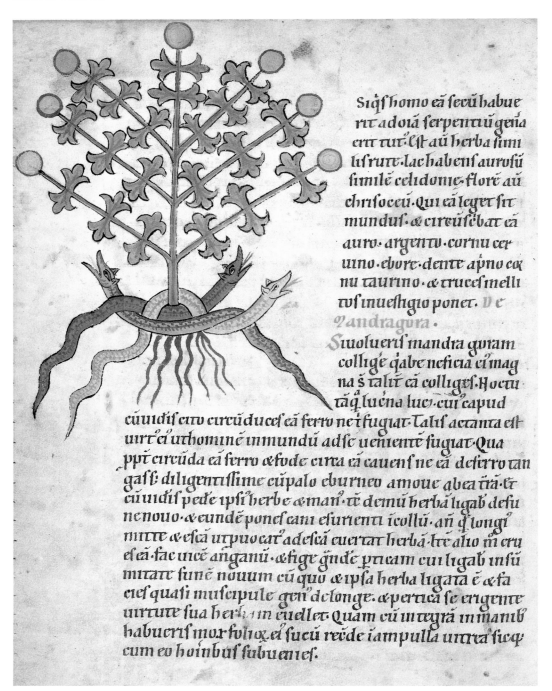

Siqf homo eã fecũ habue
rit ad oíã ferpentíũ gená
erit tut. Eft aũ herba fimi
lif rute. lac habenf aurofũ
fimilẽ celidonie. flore aũ
chrifoceũ. Qui eã legit fit
mundúf. & circũfcbat eã
auro. argentu. cornu cer
uino. ebore. dente apno cã
nu taurino. & crucefinelli
tuf inueftigio ponet. De
mandragora.
Si uoluerif mandra gurã
colligie qabe neficia eí mag
na s talit cã colligef. Hoctu
tãq̃ lucína lucí cuí capud

cũ uidíf eito circũ ducef eã ferro ne t fugiat. Talif aetanta eft
uírt eã ut homíne ínmundú adfe ueniente fugiat. Qua
ppt círcũda eã ferro & fode círca eã cauenf ne eã defirro tan
gaf f: diligentiffime cũ palo eburneo amoue abea trã. &
cũ uidíf pede ipfi herbe & man. tã demũ herbã ligab defu
ne nouo. & eundẽ ponef cam efurienti ícollú. añ q̃ longí
mitte & efcã ut puocat ad efcã euertat herbã. tre alio ín eru
efã fac ince añganũ. & fige gñde pticam cui ligab ínfũ
mitaticafune nouum cũ quo & ipfa herba ligata e & fa
cief quafi mufcipule gen de longe. & pertica fe erigente
uirtute fua herbam euellet. Quam cũ íntegrã ín manib
habuerif mox folíæ & fucũ recũde íampulla urtra fícq̃
cum eo hoínbuf fubuenief.

Mandrake from a twelfth-century copy of *Herbarium of Apuleius*. Mandrake (*Atropa mandragora*). The supposed human shape of its roots gave Mandrake a great reputation for mysterious powers. It has similar actions and toxicity to Deadly Nightshade.

jealously guarded, and also worried at the prescription of costly foreign remedies, or poisonous mineral drugs, rather than simple herbal preparations. He set about widening the knowledge of medicine, translating the London *Pharmacopoeia* in 1649 from Latin, with many additions and comments of his own.

This brought him the enmity of the physicians, which never went away, but also the admiration of the public, and it was for the latter that in 1651 he published his *English Physician*, the most successful herbal in history. The book was instantly popular and has remained in print ever since. Unlike Gerard's herbal, which was vast and contained much rambling over names and identities, necessitating much revision and cutting down for later editions, Cul-

peper's work has been reprinted largely intact.

Where Gerard was a plantsman above all, Culpeper was a practitioner. His main theoretical approach was as an astrologer, and his references to herbs is full of comments like "this is an herb of Venus" or "this is under the dominion of Mars", but it is his great practical experience that stands out over the centuries. It is still of value today to look at his comments about what a herb actually does, and for what to prescribe it.

The divide between this kind of approach, using simple herbal remedies by and large, and the practice of the physicians, who often prescribed toxic minerals or violently purging plants, continued through the seventeenth and eighteenth centuries. The latter group mainly tended the rich, and two brief examples illustrate the risks that patients ran.

In 1684, King Charles II developed a

Portrait of Leonhart Fuchs from his *De Historia Stirpium*, 1542.

LEONHARTVS FVCHSIVS
AETATIS SVAE ANNO XLI.

serious kidney infection; treatment commenced with bleeding, drawing off over a pint of blood. This was followed by emetics of antimony and vitriol, with purgatives, enemas and blistering over the next three days, before he died. In 1799, George Washington caught a feverish chill after being soaked to the skin. In the 24 hours that followed over four pints were bled out of him, he was given two large doses of calomel, a mercury compound, an antimony emetic, a cathartic enema and several blisterings, before he died. He had three physicians attending on him, whilst Charles had no less than eleven!

It is small wonder therefore that many people in Europe and America looked to other measures, and the next influential character to emerge in the history of herbalism was an American, Samuel Thomson (1769–1843). In contrast to the 'Heroic Medicine' of the regular physicians, he turned to herbs. Thomson

Honeysuckle from Gerard's *Herball*, 1636.
Honeysuckle (*Lonicera periclymenum*).
Recommended by Culpeper as a remedy for asthma, the flowers have expectorant and laxative properties. Not used today.

Portrait of John Gerard from the first edition of his *Herball*, 1597.

came from the backwoods of New Hampshire, the son of a poor farmer, and the ideas he developed were fairly simple. His mentor was a local widow, Mrs Benton, who had learned herbalism from the Indians and who had improved the health of the sickly boy when nothing else had worked. From her he learned the uses of plants, and when in turn his own child fell ill, with the doctor saying he coild do no more for her, Thomson cured her himself with steam treatment.

Thomson's view of illness was that it arose from either an imbalance and inadequacy of heat within the body, or an excess of 'morbid matter'. Consequently, his favourite treatments were steaming, a version of the Indian 'sweat-lodge', or giving cayenne pepper to stimulate heat. His other favourite was the herb *Lobelia inflata*, which in large doses induced vomiting.

Thomson's view that cold was the cause of all disease was dismissed out of hand by the physicians of the day, but his theory, however simple, came from observations of what worked, and his ideas caught hold of the American public's imagination. He studied Hippo-

Title-page from Gerard's *Herball*, 1597.

crates, bringing back the idea of the healing power of nature, and dismissed the vast purely theoretical framework of the Galenical system. He never recognized the major contribution of the Indians' medicine, but there are close parallels in their approaches.

In 1813 he established a course of instruction, patented by American law, called "Thomson's Improved System of Botanic Practice of Medicine", and his book, *The Botanic Family Physician*, became a bestseller in the USA. Throughout the country his appointed agents spread the Thomsonian methods and he attracted a great deal of support.

Following on from Thomson, his ideas were extended and developed into the approach known as physiomedicalism, and the philosophy behind this has been a potent force behind herbal medicine today. In America itself, this system disappeared in the first few years of this century under the clever onslaught of the American Medical Association. Physiomedicalism had by that time, however,

The Garden of Eden. Woodcut from the frontispiece of John Parkinson's *Paradisi in sole, Paradisus Terrestris*, 1629.

been brought across to Britain, and for that we can largely thank one of the last of the great herbalists of the past, Dr Albert Coffin.

Born in America around 1790 into a Jewish farming family, he too suffered from a severe illness, and was cured by herbal medicine, this time by a Seneca Indian woman. He enthusiastically took up the study of botanic medicine, and came to England at the beginning of Queen Victoria's reign. His ideas were very popular, especially with the working classes in the Midlands and northern England, and herbalism of this kind came to be known, rather unfortunately, as Coffinism.

His methods of spreading his system via a network of agents were very similar to Thomson's, and he published a regular journal, as well as his *Botanic Guide to Health*. His main failing, like Thomson before him, seems to have been a rigidity that could not brook different views on herbal medicine, and his high-handed approach caused rifts in the movement.

During the 1840s a serious rival to Coffin appeared in the shape of the West

Portraits of the artists H. Füllmaurer and A. Meyer from Leonhart Fuchs's *De Historia Stirpium*, 1542.

Portrait of Nicholas Culpeper from his *The Complete Herbal*, 1850.

Country herbalist John Skelton. Skelton had learnt traditional herbal medicine from his grandmother, but later went to learn from Coffin, and eventually took on some of the latter's teaching and practice when he needed a long rest.

Coffin seems to have resented Skelton's popularity, and a rift developed. This widened when Dr Wooster Beach came over from America, advocating practitioners to become doctors, from his Reformed Medical College, and Skelton adopted some of his ideas, although they too had public wrangles. Skelton was a tremendously able man, who was able to see the necessity of having an intellectual grasp on the medical sciences that were already beginning to reform the disastrous regular medicine, in a way that Coffin never could. He also tried his best to heal the divisions within the herbalists' ranks, and his influence can be seen in the establishment in 1864 of the National Association, later Institute, of Medical Herbalists.

The path of herbal medicine, from its earliest beginnings in classical history to the start of the recent revival in this country, is thus sprinkled with the names of great herbalists who have increased our knowledge of plants and their uses, and developed a system of treatment that has undergone the longest clinical trials in history. The drive and enthusiasm of these figures stand out, but underneath them are countless thousands of others who simply got on with the job of giving herbal remedies to their patients, for the very good reason that they worked.

CHAPTER III

# *The Recent Revival*

The twentieth century has seen a tremendous change in the fortunes of herbal medicine, both in this country and elsewhere. In the first fifty years, the rapid increase in pharmaceutical products, combined with pressure from the conventional medics, led to a decline in the use of herbs. The social upheavals of the late nineteenth century, and then the First World War, meant that the knowledge and domestic use of simple herbal remedies was to a large extent lost, and the NIMH had constantly to fend off attempts to bring in restrictive legislation and create a medical monopoly.

Even at this time, however, there were some very positive signs. The legal battles that took place brought out tremendous public support for herbal medicine, which surprised and shook the government of the day, and demonstrated the widespread belief and trust in the value of herbs.

In the first quarter of the century, one of the most significant of new herbals was written by Mrs Grieve, with an encyclopaedic volume of information about herbs, both from that time and historically. The book's editor, Hilda Leyel, also started a lay organization, now called the Herb Society, for anyone interested in herbs and which still

flourishes today, with a varied and interesting quarterly journal.

However, the great revival in herbal matters has really only taken off since the 1960s. A good measure of this renewed interest has been due to the increasing disillusionment that people were feeling by this time with the orthodox medical establishment. A series of 'wonder drugs' had come and gone, with the side-effects becoming more apparent with time, culminating in the Thalidomide tragedy.

Not only were the public looking for treatments that carried fewer side-effects, something that very much continues today, people began to be wary of the potentially addictive nature of some of the newer drugs. The so-called minor tranquillizers, especially the benzodiazepine group typified by Valium and Ativan, have been prescribed in such large numbers, and for such long stretches of time, that they have created a sub-culture of people reliant on them but desperately seeking to break the habit. In common with other forms of therapy, herbal medicine has become a popular and successful way to return to a drug-free life.

The other major impetus in the search for alternatives to conventional medicine was the perceived lack of care and understanding by the orthodox medical profession. The work pressures on doctors have resulted for instance in Britain of an average consultation times by a general practitioner of six minutes, long waiting lists for hospital and consultant appointments, and repeat prescriptions for symptoms without attention to the indi-

vidual. These have created strong feelings of disenchantment in the public. In America and on the Continent healthcare is largely private, but there has been a similar trend towards an impersonal,

Larger Chives (*Allium schoenoprasum*) from *Curtis's Botanical Magazine*. Introduced by the Romans, chives have many of the properties of garlic, in a milder form. Their equally mild flavour may suit some people better, and they are excellent in stimulating appetite and digestion in convalescence.

Opposite: Sunflower (*Helianthus annuus*) by John Miller from his *Illustratio sexualis — An Illustration of the Sexual System of the Genera Plantarum of Linnaeus*, 1777. Introduced into Britain in the sixteenth century from Peru, where it was revered as a symbol of the Sun God. The seeds have valuable amounts of polyunsaturated oils, and are useful in food for both people or animals.

170

*Mentha viridis*

Published by Dr Woodville. Oct. 1.1792.

171

*Mentha Pulegium*

Published by Dr Woodville. Nov. 1.1792.

Spearmint *Mentha viridis* from Woodville's *Medical Botany*, 1790. Spearmint (*Mentha spicata*). This is also similar in actions to peppermint, and was brought to Britain by the Romans, who cultivated it over large areas. It is grown for used in food, as a tea and/or for medicinal purposes in a large number of countries.

Pennyroyal (*Mentha pulegium*) from Woodville's *Medical Botany*. Used a great deal in the past in medicine, it has similar actions to peppermint. It is, however, more stimulating to the uterine muscles, and should be avoided in pregnancy.

high technology but low human interest system of treatment.

By contrast, medical herbalists give much more time to allow a full picture to emerge of each person's problems, and there is great emphasis on looking at all aspects of the individual's lifestyle for causative factors in illness. The linking of different aspects together, in order to create a jigsaw that also makes sense to the patient, is one of the great attractions of the herbalist's approach, and has played a significant part in the recent move towards herbal medicine.

Alongside the increased interest in seeking herbal treatment has come a greater awareness of herbs generally. The sale of herbal remedies, herb teas and other products has grown at an astonishing rate. In many countries, for example on the Continent and in the USA, the herbal practitioner had been largely legislated away, or subsumed into conventional medicine with an inevitable watering down of the herbs' uses, and the dominant way of using herbs has been on a self-help basis.

Whilst this is a poor substitute for seeing a medical herbalist, especially in the case of anything more than minor ailments, domestic use of herbal remedies has nevertheless been a powerful force in the revival of herbalism. For example, by the year 1979, sales of herbal products in the USA had grown from a very low level to more than $150,000,000. In Europe, from Germany to Holland the picture is the same, and in Britain too herbal suppliers have mushroomed in the last twenty years.

With all this renewed activity the development of research and scientific enquiry into plants has also begun to grow. The major drug companies have sporadically looked towards plants as sources for medicines, but find it cheaper, easier and more profitable to stay in the laboratory. As always, the

Pl. 23.

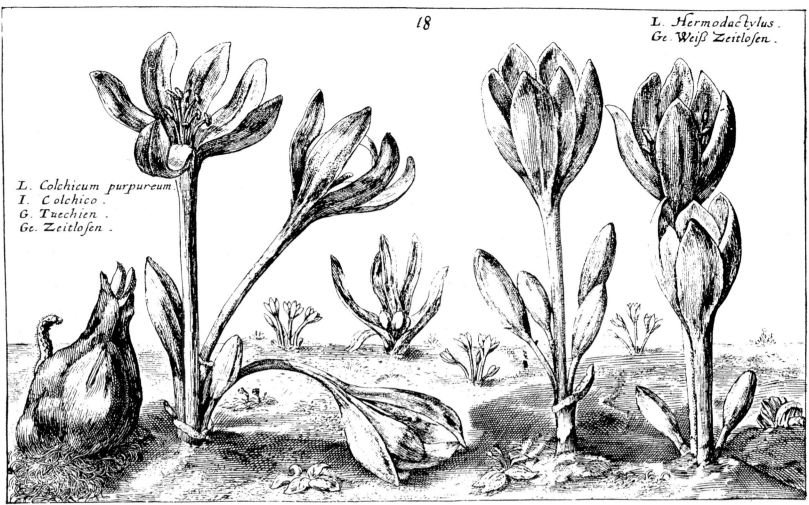

*18*

L. *Colchicum purpureum.*
I. *Colchico.*
G. *Tucchien.*
Ge. *Zeitlofen.*

L. *Hermodactylus.*
Ge. *Weiß Zeitlofen.*

Common Saffron from *Hortus Floridus*, Crispin de Pass, 1614.

herbal professions have very little money, but much has been done already. There is a British *Herbal Pharmacopoeia*, now under revision, to give authoritative information on the herbs, and a major new initiative, the European Scientific Cooperative on Phytotherapy (ESCOP), is linking the national bodies and has started to prepare a European *Herbal Pharmacopoeia*.

The NIMH has launched a research fund, and is linking up with Exeter

Previous page: Saffron Crocus (*Crocus sativus*) has been highly valued, and valuable, since earliest times; it was mentioned in the Song of Solomon. The finest yellow colouring for food, with its own delicate flavour, it takes around sixty thousand stigmas to make one pound of the spice. Saffron Crocus (*Crocus sativus*) from Mrs Loudon's *The Ladies' Flower-Garden of Ornamental Bulbous Plants*, 1841. 1. *Crocus speciosus* 2. *C. sativus* 3. *C. biflorus* 4. *C. serotinus* 5. *C. susianus* 6. *C. versicolor.*

University to develop a worldwide database on herbal research. The recent review by the Department of Health of licences for over-the-counter herbal medicines has at least the benefit of stimulating rigorous evaluation of the remedies by the companies involved. There is a great sense of herbal medicine 'getting its house in order'.

On the wider front, so much interest has been generated in herbs and wild flowers that demand for information and access has seemed to outstrip supply. There are a number of new herbals and books on all aspects of using herbs, from gardening through cookery to medicine.

Growing herbs has not been so popular since Tudor times; all the catalogues and flower shows have sections on herbs. Each year at the Chelsea Flower Show recently more herbs have been used in the display gardens, some of them given over entirely to wild plants. Apart from the delight in growing them for their own sake, gardeners also want a

useful herb border. The virtual rediscovery of herbs in cooking in this country in the last twenty years, influenced by the long tradition of using them in other countries such as France or Italy, has led to many people wanting to have them fresh from their own garden.

The word 'natural' has been rather overplayed in the last few years, covering a multitude of different areas, but herbs of course fit this idea perfectly. An awareness of the loss of much of our wild habitat, the destruction of the rainforest and other environmental concerns have given us a keener appreciation of nature, and a wish to save and enjoy it.

For most people, herbal medicine is seen as both more natural in its widest sense and safer. It should be stated clearly that many plants are poisonous, as some in this book will show, and all herbal remedies should be treated with respect. Nothing is absolutely safe; however, the record of medical herbalists is impeccable, especially in comparison

*Tropaeolum majus*

Nasturtium (*Tropaeolum majus*) from Woodville's *Medical Botany*. Nasturtium leaves are very high in Vitamin C, and they have a long tradition of use on the Continent as a natural antibiotic. They have a peppery taste and can be used as a substitute for it, or chopped up in salads for added pungency.

herbal remedies, along with an appreciation of their practical value now, has been an important factor in public support for and the revived use of herbal medicine. Together with other areas of interest, this has ensured that herbs are again a part of everyday life, if not at the level of some periods of our history at least on a secure footing.

The history of herbal plants is a fascinating one, embracing every time and culture, and herbs have contributed enormously to human knowledge, health and happiness over the centuries. The traditional folk medicine systems around the world continue to provide the major form of health-care, based firmly on using herbal remedies. More sophisticated systems of herbal medicine, such as Chinese, Indian and, especially for us, Western medical herbalism also flourish. Their roots stretch back to the earliest human civilizations, but they have flowered again in the present. Herbal medicine has an impressive past, but equally it has an exciting future.

Common Rue *Ruta graveolens* from Woodville's *Medical Botany*, 1790.

*Ruta graveolens.*

Published by Dr Woodville, August 1. 1790.

with orthodox medicine. Herbal medicines can certainly be robust in their action, but they present nothing like the problems which modern drugs are constantly shown to do.

Herbal medicines tend to act in a slower way, helping the body's defences to restore it to health. They are generally very well tolerated, and occasionally can be seen to act almost like foods, providing the essential elements that a person needs to be able to get back in balance.

The concept of balance is an integral one to herbal medicine, and therefore treatment involves much more than simply treating the obvious symptoms.

The chemical complexity of herbs means that they have a more rounded action than the intended 'magic bullet' approach that it was hoped conventional drugs were to achieve. This latter idea has largely been left behind, but it is still true that herbal medicines have a wider degree of efficacy. A plant such as Chamomile, for instance, may exert an anti-inflammatory action on the digestive tract, whilst also improving digestive functions, acting as a general relaxant and reducing muscle spasms.

The memory of centuries of reliance on

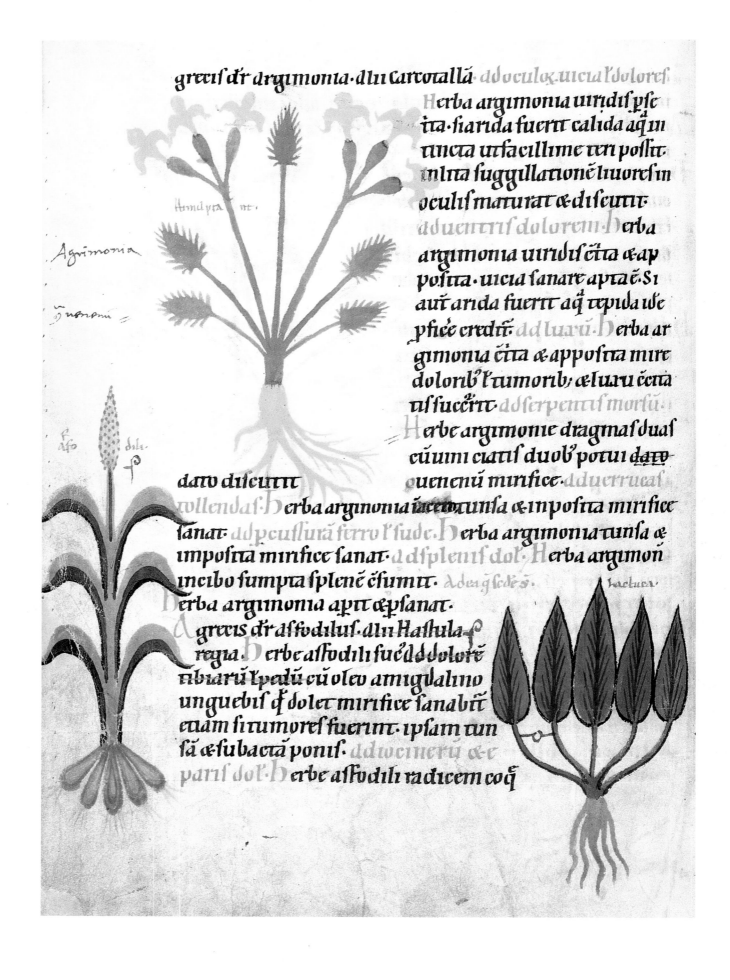

grecis dr argimonia · dlii carcotalla · add oculox uicia l dolores

Herba argimonia uiridis pse
tta · si arida fuerit calida aq̃ in
tincta ut facillime teri possit ·
in ita suggillationē liuores in
oculis maturat & discutit ·
ad uentris dolorem · Herba
argimonia uiridis ētta & ap
posita · uicia sanare apta ē · Si
aut arida fuerit aq̃ tepida ide
pfice creditr̃ · ad luxū · Herba ar
gimonia ētta & apposita mire
doloribʒ l̃ tumoribʒ & luxu ētta
tis succr̃it · ad serpentis morsū ·
Herbe argimonie dragmas duas
cū uini ciatis duobʒ potui dato
ouenenū mirifice · ad uerrucas
tollendas · Herba argimonia iacetotunsa & inposita mirifice
sanat · ad percussurā ferro l̃ sude · Herba argimonia tunsa &
imposita mirifice sanat · ad splenis dol̃ · Herba argimoñ
incibo sumpta splenē cōsumit · ad eā q̃ sede ñ
Herba argimonia apta & psanat ·

Agrimonia

in uenenū

dato discutit

f argimonia

dili

Agrecis dr asfodilus · dlii Hastula
regia · Herbe asfodili suc̃ dd dolorē
tibiarū l̃ pedū cū oleo amigdalino
unguebis q̃ dolet mirifice sanabit
etiam si tumores fuerint · ipsam tun
sa & subacta ponis · ad doceineriū & e
paris dol̃ · Herbe asfodili radicem coq̃

lactuca

# CHAPTER IV

# Herbs

## Agrimony

*Agrimonia eupatoria*, Rosaceae

### DESCRIPTION

Agrimony is a common plant, widespread throughout Europe, Asia and North America. It particularly likes wasteland and dry hedge-banks or fieldsides. The upright stem grows to a height of one to two feet and carries long, slender spikes of yellow flowers from June to September. The leaves are quite distinctive, being pinnate in shape — i.e., they are divided into pairs of leaflets. This is especially noticeable in the large, lower leaves, which can be up to nine inches long.

The whole plant is a deep green colour, and is usually clothed all over with fine hairs. There is a slightly fruity aroma, particularly from the flowers, although even the dried leaves retain some of the odour. The seed-vessels have a circle of hooked spines that often cling to people and animals, and give it country names such as Cockleburr or Sticklewort.

### HISTORY AND ORIGINS

Agrimony has a very long history as a medicinal plant; indeed, its name comes from the Greek Argemone, referring to its uses for eye problems, and from the semi-mythical king Mithridates Eupator,

Opposite: Agrimony from a twelfth-century copy of *Herbarium of Apuleius*.

Agrimony *Agrimonia eupatoria* Woodville's *Medical Botany*, 1790.

*Agrimonia Eupatoria*

Published by D.ᵣ Woodville, Oct.ʳ 1, 1790.

Agrimony from Gerard's *Herball*.

who was renowned for his herbal wisdom.

Its most well-known property was as a vulnerary, or wound-healer; Dioscorides wrote that it was good for "such as are bitten with serpents", while Pliny termed Agrimony "a herb of princely authority". The Anglo-Saxons regarded it highly for all manner of wounds and bites, and later writers speak of it as a remedy for internal bleeding too.

In the Middle Ages it was an important ingredient in the so-called 'arquebusade water', a preparation made for dressing wounds made by this ancient weapon (an arquebus, or harquebus, being an early type of portable gun). Culpeper describes its actions in detail, saying it "openeth and cleanseth the liver, helpeth the jaundice, and is very beneficial to the bowels, healing all inward wounds, bruises, hurts, and other distempers".

This reputation for benefitting the liver is also noted by many other writers: for instance, Dr Hill in the late eighteenth century describes an infusion of the root

as a treatment for jaundice and malarial-type fevers, in times past called 'the ague'. Several Indian tribes in North America and Canada have used Agrimony for fevers, and valued it highly in this context.

Apart from its medicinal uses, Agrimony has been valuable as a source of a yellow dye, the whole plant being used. If the dye is fixed with a mordant such as chrome, the colour becomes more fawn-like.

### CULTIVATION

Since Agrimony grows so prolifically on wasteland and in hedge-banks, it is scarcely necessary to cultivate it. In general it likes a dry, sunny position, with no special requirements as to soil.

### MODERN MEDICINAL USES

Agrimony contains tannins, bitters, silica and essential oil, and these give it its characteristic actions of astringency and digestive tonic. The traditional uses as a tonic for the liver are confirmed by modern practice, and it is suitable for a range of mild digestive disturbances. As a tissue healer and gentle diuretic, it is also prescribed for cystitis. Gargling with agrimony, especially as a tincture, is helpful for toning up sore throats. The whole plant, above ground, is used.

The main indications for use are:

■ Digestive upsets and infections, including children's ailments, especially where accompanied by diarrhoea.
■ Excessive acidity in the stomach, particularly when associated with inflammation of the gall-bladder.
■ Cystitis with great frequency of urination.
■ Skin eruptions when the digestion is weak or liver function is poor.
■ Sore throats and laryngitis, as a gargle.
■ General sluggishness — as a 'spring tonic' to stimulate better digestion and cleansing.

## *Angelica*

*Angelica archangelica*, Umbelliferae

### DESCRIPTION

Angelica is thought to have been originally a native of the Middle East, but in much earlier times it spread northwards into cooler climates, and became naturalized in Scandinavia. It then came to the rest of Europe and into Britain from these northerly latitudes during the Middle Ages. It thrives in moist, shady places, often being found by rivers.

It is a large plant, often growing to six feet and more. Technically it is a biennial, but it may not flower until the third year of growth, or even later; having set seed it soon dies. The strong stem is hollow and fluted in shape, whilst the leaf stalks are also hollow, and enlarged at the base. The very large leaves are bright green and highly divided.

The huge umbels carry small, green-yellow flowers, which are followed by

Garden Angelica from Gerard's *Herball*.

*Tab. 191.*

ANGELICA ARCHANGELICA.L.
Die edle Engelwurz.

Garden Angelica *Angelica archangelica* Joseph Jakob
Plenck's *Icones plantarum medicinalium*, 1788–1812.

very pale brown oblong fruits. The whole plant has a most distinctive aromatic odour and taste, quite different from most members of the Umbelliferae family, such as Fennel or Dill. This odour is also found in the thick, fleshy root, which is one of the most important parts medicinally. The taste is quite sweet, and indeed the stem and seeds have long been used in confectionery.

HISTORY AND ORIGINS

Angelica has a very high reputation in the traditional medicines of all the northern European countries, and has been held in high esteem for many centuries. The very name indicates its associations with healing, and supposed angelic qualities. These included protection from infections, epidemics and poisons, and for purifying the blood.

Mediaeval writers waxed lyrical over its properties; Parkinson placed it foremost in his *Paradise in Sole* (a play on his own name — the literal translation being 'park in sun') in 1629. Culpeper declared that the stems and roots "are good preservatives in time of infection; and at other times to warm and comfort a cold stomach…(it) helpeth the pleurisy, as also all other diseases of the lungs and breast". He further valued it for digestive problems, and in typically flowing style stated that it "openeth the stoppage of the liver and spleen, and briefly easeth and discusseth all windiness and inward swellings".

Folk medicine placed a good deal of faith in Angelica, wherever such knowledge persisted, through to this century. For instance, Angelica has grown in London for many years as a naturalized escape, and sites such as Lincoln's Inn Fields and the slopes of the Tower of London were formerly valuable harvesting areas.

It has not only been for medicine that Angelica is prized; candied Angelica is still a delicious ingredient in top quality fruit cakes, jams and so forth. In the past the roots were used in Scandinavia for making bread, and the raw stems are occasionally still chewed in rural areas. It is also one of the ingredients in the old, secret herbal recipe for Chartreuse. In fact, Angelica demonstrates the blurring of distinction between food and medicine that existed for centuries until modern medicine.

## CULTIVATION

Angelica will thrive best in a shady place, in moderately rich, damp soil, but it is really quite adaptable and can do well in sandy soil too. The seed loses its power of germination very quickly, and it may be better to buy a young plant and either select self-sown seedlings or propagate by root division. Give Angelica plenty of space, the final distance between plants ·may need to be five feet.

## MODERN MEDICINAL USES

One of the major constituents of Angelica are the volatile oils that give the characteristic odour and action as carminative, digestive tonic, reducing flatulence and spasm, and inducing a feeling of warmth. It is also an expectorant, and gently promotes sweating in feverish conditions. From these properties it is easy to see that Angelica has many applications, the main indications for use being:

■ Convalescence from debilitating illness, especially when the person feels chilled.
■ Indigestion with flatulence, poor appetite and/or sluggish liver.
■ Bronchial coughs that are unproductive, ranging from children's respiratory infections to bronchial asthma.
■ Respiratory infections that lead to a fevered state. A hot poultice of the leaves or a hot compress on the chest is an old and very effective method of giving relief in pleurisy.

All parts of the plant have been used, the root at times appearing in European pharmacopoeias as an official medicine. Nowadays, the root or the seeds are most significant medicinally, although the leaf is used too.

Mountain Arnica *Arnica montana* Woodville's *Medical Botany*, 1790.

# Arnica

*Arnica montana*, Compositae

## DESCRIPTION

Arnica is a native of alpine pastures and mountain woodlands throughout central Europe. It may rarely be found as an escape in the highest mountainous areas of England and southern Scotland, and is also found in similar regions of North America.

The plant is a perennial, with a creeping rhizome which gives rise to a flat rosette of pale green, ovate leaves. From the centre of these the flowering stem rises, in the second year, growing up to two feet high, carrying paired leaves and topped by a flower of bright orange-yellow. The plant is aromatic.

Arnica montana

Published as the Act directs by Dr Woodville Jan.y. 1. 1790.

### HISTORY AND ORIGINS

Arnica has a long and powerful tradition in folk medicine in those countries where it is indigenous. It has been used as an external application for sprains, bruises and other injuries, *where the skin is unbroken*, and has deservedly been called the skier's companion; Maurice Messegue called it the "tumbler's cure-all". Many recipes for home-made ointments have been handed down in families of mountain guides, often using goat butter as the base for the preparation.

European herbal traditions also extol its virtues internally in *small* quantities for fevers and to stimulate the circulation. They are always careful to stress the need to limit dosage, and to strain an infusion through a fine cloth to remove the fine, irritating pappus, or hairs, that can affect the throat. Even so, the potential for toxicity has led to disagreements in the past over whether it should be used internally at all.

The Abbé Kneipp, who in the nineteenth century re-established hydrotherapy and naturopathy on the Continent, clearly thought it was worth taking the precautions in dosage and prescribing for its value, and wrote: "Arnica is known throughout the entire world as an excellent medicinal plant. What I cannot understand is why this is disputed by so many people who could and should know better".

Its main use internally has been in homoeopathic medicine, however, and the minute doses prescribed in this system mean that it is perfectly safe to take. The prime homoeopathic recommendations for Arnica are for states of shock, whether from falls, accidents, etc., or emotional shocks.

In olden times, Arnica leaves were smoked instead of tobacco, hence the country name of Mountain Tobacco. The freshly crushed flowers were employed as a kind of snuff, and in France it has been called Sneezewort.

### CULTIVATION

Arnica will only really thrive in the acid, peaty soils of mountainous regions; Palaiseul suggests that it only grows at altitudes between 3,500 feet and 8,500 feet. However, it may be cultivated (probably as an annual) in a mixture of peat, loam and sand if sown in early spring, perhaps in a cold frame, and planted out in May.

The flowerheads are collected between June and August; in some parts the roots have also been employed, and these would be collected in autumn after the leaves have died down.

### MODERN MEDICINAL USES

Arnica is *only used externally* today in herbal medicine; for internal uses homoeopathic dilutions are needed for safety. Its prime external indications are, as always, for bruising, sprains and so forth. The flowers contain constituents which stimulate the peripheral blood supply and promote healing when used locally. It should only be used on unbroken skin, and care should be taken to look out for any signs of dermatitis, in which case the applications must be discontinued.

Despite such cautionary notes, it is quickly and highly effective for many injuries.

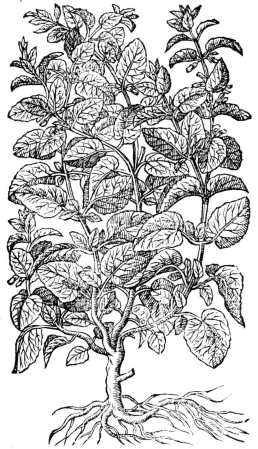

## Balm

*Melissa officinalis*, Labiatae

### DESCRIPTION

Frequently called Lemon Balm because of its wonderful lemony fragrance, Balm was originally a native of southern Europe, but was introduced into Britain at a very early stage and is now grown in gardens around the world.

The square, branching stems grow to two or three feet, with pairs of bright-green leaves at each joint. These look rather like mint, but with a distinctive odour and taste. The small white flowers grow out of the leaf axils in late summer.

Although the plant dies down in winter, the roots are perennial, if the leaves are picked for tea in the summer months, Balm can form quite a sizeable bushy shape, seeding itself around the garden.

### HISTORY AND ORIGINS

The name Melissa derives from the Greek for honey-bee, and the plant has long

Common Balm and Turkey Balm from Gerard's *Herball*.

147

Common Balm *Melissa officinalis* Woodville's *Medical Botany*, 1790.

ingredient of Carmelite water, drunk for its reviving properties by many in the past, for example the Emperor Charles V.

All the old writers extolled its virtues; Avicenna said that it made the heart merry and joyful and strengthened the vital spirits. Culpeper wrote: "(Balm) driveth away all troublesome cares and thoughts out of the mind, arising from melancholy and black choler".

An interesting ancient use was as a dressing for wounds, especially in battle. Gerard again quotes Pliny and Dioscorides when he says that it "is most singular to heale up greene wounds that are cut with yron; it cureth the rupture in short time". Mrs Grieve points out that by early this century it was recognized that "the balsamic oils of aromatic plants make excellent dressings: they give off ozone and thus exercise anti-putrescent effects".

## CULTIVATION

Balm is a very easy plant to grow, although it is best sited in a warm, sunny spot with a reasonably moisture-retentive soil. It can be propagated by seeds, cuttings or by division of the roots. The seeds should be sown in spring and the plants will be ready to set out in late August. Give the plants plenty of space to allow the leaves to develop, and to avoid the fungus attacks that can occur in damp weather.

## MODERN MEDICINAL USES

Balm is an excellent gentle relaxant, both for nervous tension and anxiety, and for tension-related indigestion. The volatile oil is probably most important medicinally, and the tea from the fresh plant makes a very useful drink, morning and night. Its mildness means that it can be useful for children's upsets due to restlessness and over-excitement.

The kind of problems that Balm may be prescribed for include nervous dyspepsia, anxiety and stress, depression resulting from chronic tensions, pre-menstrual tensions, insomnia and so on. Since it helps to induce sweating, it is also valuable in influenza, particularly where there is irritability and difficulty in sleeping.

been used by bee-keepers to attract a swarm by rubbing fresh leaves on a new hive, and grown as a bee plant. Gerard says: "It is profitably planted in Gardens, as Pliny writeth, about places where Bees are kept, because they are delighted with this herbe above others." Balm itself is a shortening of Balsam, or 'most sweet of oils'.

Balm had a great reputation in olden times (and is one of the author's favourite remedies today) for all complaints of the nervous system. Paracelsus rated it highly, and believed it could completely revive a person. As a stress-reducer, it thus gained a reputation for inducing longevity; for instance, John Hussey, who lived to an apparent 116 years, breakfasted for fifty years on Balm and honey. Spirit of Balm was the principal

# Borage

*Borago officinalis*, Boraginaceae

## Description

Borage stems from the Mediterranean area, but is naturalized in most European countries and elsewhere, although it probably spread as a garden escape. It is mostly found on waste ground, but has been grown for centuries for culinary and medicinal uses.

The whole plant is covered with thick, white, prickly hairs. The hollow stems grow to some two feet, and are quite succulent in appearance when broken.

*217*

*Borago officinalis*

*Publiſhed by Dᴿ Woodville, Febʸ 1, 1794.*

Borage *Borago officinalis* Woodville's *Medical Botany*, 1790.

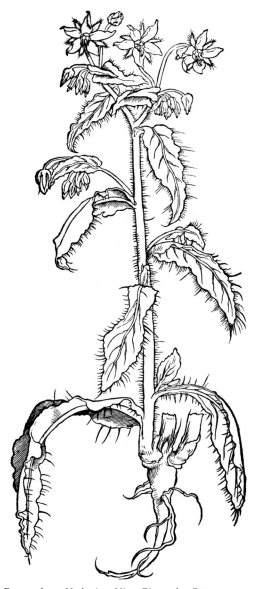

Borage from *Herbarium Vivae Eicones* by Otto Brunfels, 1537.

The large, deep-green leaves are rough and stinging to the touch; the lower leaves are stalked.

The most distinctive part of Borage is the flowers; these are shaped like a five-pointed star, and range in colour from an initial purplish-pink to a bright Madonna blue. They hang in drooping clusters, and have prominent black anthers which form a central cone. The herb has a cool, cucumber fragrance.

## History and Origins

The name is considered to be a corruption of the Latin *corago*, derived from *cor*, the heart, and *ago*, I bring, referring to its cordial effects. Gerard quotes a very old rhyme, *Ego Borago gaudia semper ago* — I, Borage, bring always courage — and he says: that "The leaves and floures of Borage put into wine make men and women glad and merry, driving away all sadnessse, dulnesse, and melancholy."

Most ancient writers affirm these properties; Evelyn states: "Sprigs of Borage

41

are of known virtue to revive the hypochondriac and cheer the hard student." Culpeper recommends it as a great cordial, while Parkinson advises it "to expel pensiveness and melanchollie".

Both leaves and flowers have similar reputations, and both have been employed in home remedies. The leaves were frequently steeped in wine and cider, and there are many recipes from Britain, Europe and America for using them in claret cup and other cordial drinks. Here is an older remedy: One bottle of claret, one pint bottle of German Seltzer-water, a small bunch of balm, ditto of borage, one orange cut in slices, half a cucumber sliced thick, a liqueur glass of Cognac, and one ounce of bruised sugar-candy. Place all the ingredients in a jug which is immersed in ice, stir and leave for an hour before straining off the herbs etc. (from Francatelli's *Cook's Guide*, quoted by Mrs Grieve).

Still today, the leaves and more notably the flowers are put into summer punches and cocktails for their flavour and the colour of the flowers; they make a Pimms into something extra special! In Victorian times the flowers were candied to preserve them and used as food decorations, or the syrup given to people in convalescence.

### CULTIVATION

As an annual, Borage can only be propagated by seed, but this is hardly a drawback since it self-seeds so prolifically that the major difficulty is weeding out the excess! It prefers a sunny, well-drained position and will grow even on quite light soils.

The plant needs a good deal of space to fully develop, and may swamp smaller plants. Borage can flower right through a mild winter, but frosts turn it into a soggy, black heap that should be put into the compost pile as it contains quantities of minerals. In warm areas it is possible to raise two generations in one season, as it has a short cycle; picking and trimming the plants can help them not to look so straggly.

### MODERN MEDICINAL USES

One of the principal actions of Borage is as a restorative and tonic for the adrenal cortex. This can be especially valuable following prolonged stress or treatment with steroids, and accounts for its reputation as a general tonic, helping people cope better with stress.

The high mucilage content, in common with other members of this family such as Comfrey, has proved useful in external applications for inflammatory conditions, and internally for an inflamed respiratory tract, although this is less used now than other remedies.

## Burdock

*Arctium lappa*, Compositae

### DESCRIPTION

Burdock grows freely throughout Europe and North America in field borders, roadsides, waste ground and damp hedgerows. It is a substantial plant, growing to five or six feet, with very large leaves at the base forming a rosette and smaller ones growing up the stem. The leaves are covered on the underside with a mass of fine down, giving a grey colour.

The round heads of its purple flowers show it clearly to belong to the thistle group; they are borne in clusters, and are covered with many stiff, hooked bracts which stick to fur and clothes on contact and give it its name. The original Greek names are *arktos*, meaning 'bear' in reference to the roughness of its burs, and *lappa*, to seize.

The fleshy roots are thick and can run straight down for nearly three feet. They have a slightly sweetish taste at first, but with an underlying bitterness. The overall appearance of the plant can vary considerably, and botanists argue whether there are sub-species or separate species, but medicinally there does not seem to be any great distinction.

### HISTORY AND ORIGINS

The distinctive burs of Burdock have been the source of many old country names and references. Shakespeare seems particularly to delight in using them as metaphors; for instance, in *Troilus and Cressida* Pandarus says: "They are Burs, I can tell you, they'll stick where they are thrown".

Also, in *As You Like It* we can hear:

*Rosalind:* How full of briers is this working-day world!
*Celia:* They are but burs, cousin, thrown upon thee in holiday foolery. If we walk not in the trodden paths, our very petticoats will catch them.

In times past, the stalks of Burdock were sometimes eaten as a vegetable, the rind being stripped off and then the stalks boiled; occasionally, they were candied, rather like Angelica. Culpeper mentions something similar when he says "The root may be preserved with sugar, and taken fasting or at other times."

The traditional medicinal areas of use are largely those which are employed today, specifically in a wide range of skin conditions. Burdock was considered one of the prime 'alteratives'; this is a term which is difficult to translate into conventional medical language, a more modern term being 'blood-cleanser'. Essentially, Burdock and similar herbs are seen to improve the quality of the supply of nutrients in the bloodstream to the growing layers of the skin, and to improve the removal of waste matter from these tissues.

Different traditions used the roots, leaves or seeds for chronic skin conditions. In America the seeds were most commonly used; their oiliness was thought to be very useful in restoring smoothness to the skin in dry, scaly conditions like eczema. In Britain the root is more frequently mentioned, although the medieval Welsh Physicians of Myddfai suggested for 'squamous eruption' (probably psoriasis): "Take the leaves of burdock, pound them well with a little wine and strain. Take three spoonfuls, night, morning and noon, and let a decoction of burdock be your only drink."

A complaint that seems to have been fairly frequent in the Middle Ages is kidney or bladder stones, and Burdock

Opposite: Burdock *Arctium lappa* Woodville's *Medical Botany*, 1790.

Pl. 24.

*Arctium Lappa.*

W.H.Lizars sculp!

was regarded as one of the best remedies for this. Here, the seeds are generally advised, Culpeper writing: "The seed is much commended to break the stone, and cause it to be expelled by urine, and is often used with other seeds and things for that purpose." The use of other seeds, usually of a hard, stony nature, was an example of treating 'like with like', which was popular at the time.

### CULTIVATION

The fact that Burdock grows so freely in hedgerows, riversides, etc., means that there has never been a great need to cultivate it. Most soil types are suitable, although the roots will be largest in a fairly light and well-drained soil. Since they can go down to two or three feet, harvesting is also likely to be easier in such soil.

### MODERN MEDICINAL USES

The action of Burdock as a general cleanser has already been mentioned; since it also has diuretic and mild laxative properties, the plant is appropriate for many conditions of excess toxin accumulation, such as boils and other inflammatory skin disorders. It is a valuable remedy for many people with eczema, especially when in the dry phases, or psoriasis, although dosage should start fairly low and be increased as the process of elimination is improved. The root is considered more powerful in its actions than the leaves.

# Caraway

*Carum carvii*, Umbelliferae

### DESCRIPTION

Caraway grows in the wild throughout Europe and Asia, as far as India, and also in parts of Canada and the USA, yet it is only cultivated in small areas of these regions; England is one of these areas, and it is slowly becoming naturalized from garden escapes over the centuries.

Caraway is a biennial, with a thick, tapering tap root and smooth, branching

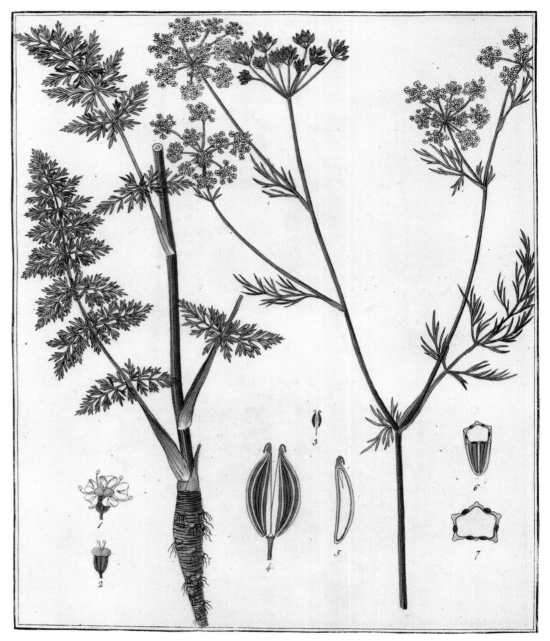

Caraway *Carum carui* from *Getreue Darstellung…Arzneykunde…*, F.G. Haynes 1821.

stems reaching some two feet high. The leaves are pinnate and finely divided, and the umbels of white flowers ripen through July to produce the long, curved seeds that are the parts used.

### HISTORY AND ORIGINS

Caraway has been famous since classical antiquity; there are references to it as long ago as 1500 BC in lists of herbs brought by the ancient Egyptians. The Arabs called it *Karawya*, hence the ordinary name, and

still use the seeds today.

It was valued greatly as a flavouring as well as for its medicinal properties. In the huge Roman feasts, caraway 'comfits', dipped in sugar, were served to aid digestion and relieve flatulence between courses. Shakespeare has Squire Shallow invite Falstaff to a "pippin and dish of caraways" in *Henry IV*.

In Germany and Scandinavia Caraway seeds have been used for centuries in various dishes such as cabbage, soups, cakes and breads. The liqueur Kümmel is flavoured from the seeds, as are other cordials. They have an unmistakable flavour which is either loved or detested.

Medicinally, the seeds, or more accurately fruits, have always been known as one of the best carminatives (i.e., for dispelling wind and bloating). Culpeper says that the seed "is conducing to all cold griefs of the head and stomach, bowels, or mother, as also the wind in them" and especially recommends the confects, or seeds, dipped in sugar. Parkinson makes similar suggestions, and they are a good example of how food and medicine have been considered inextricably linked until recent times. Culpeper suggests using the roots as a vegetable: "The root is better food than the parsnips; it is pleasant and comfortable to the stomach, and helpeth digestion."

Mrs Grieve describes a quaint old belief about Caraway, that it would prevent the theft of any object which contained it, and similarly it was used a good deal in love potions to keep the lover true. This

Caraway from Gerard's *Herball*.

superstition may come from the observation that tame doves are very fond of the seed and are unlikely to leave if Caraway seeds or bread are left in their cote!

## CULTIVATION

The seeds are best sown in the early autumn, when ripened, although they may be sown in spring. In the wild, they prefer moist meadows, so a moisture-retentive soil will do best; however, if grown in full sun the seeds contain more and better quality volatile oils. An autumn sowing will produce seeds the following year.

## MODERN MEDICINAL USES

The volatile oil is the active part medicinally, and the seeds have carminative and anti-spasmodic properties. They are thus mainly prescribed for flatulent dyspepsia and colic, much as in the past. They do have some value as an expectorant for chesty coughs and bronchitis. They may also be taken as a tea or even chewed, particularly for indigestion, and for infantile colic may be given to the mother if she is breast-feeding.

Caraway seeds contain a little tannin, and may be used for minor instances of diarrhoea, especially where there is also a lot of intestinal gas. This astringency may be of value as a gargle, but herbal practitioners are likely to use other, more powerful, remedies in this way.

# Castor Oil plant

*Ricinus communis*, Euphorbiaceae

## DESCRIPTION

The Castor Oil plant is originally a native of India, but has spread from there to be cultivated in many regions of the world. In tropical climates it grows into a tree of some thirty or forty feet, although it will only reach around ten feet or so in Mediterranean countries. In England it is grown as an annual shrubby plant of around four feet.

The large, palmate leaves grow alternately on purplish stalks; the young ones are reddish, expanding into the bluish-green mature leaves that make it an attractive ornamental plant. The male and female flowers appear together on the same panicle. The fruit is green and deeply grooved, while the seeds that develop within are oval and grey-brown. The seeds themselves are *poisonous* and highly irritant to the digestive tract, and should never be taken.

## HISTORY AND ORIGINS

The Castor Oil plant, and the uses of the oil extracted from the seeds, has been known from very ancient times. Herodotus wrote about it in the fourth century BC, and says that it was already much used by the Egyptians — tomb excavations often unearth the seeds as part of the medicine chest for the departed soul. The Greeks called it *Kiki*, and similar names crop up in other Eastern civilizations, for instance the *Kikajon* mentioned in the Bible. All the Greek and Roman writers recognized its dangers as a drastic purgative.

Its medicinal uses continued until the Middle Ages, for instance by the celebrated thirteenth-century herbalist and cleric Albertus Magnus, but it steadily declined in usage, due partly to its irritant effects on the bowels and also largely to its nauseating flavour. This is probably still remembered today by older people from their childhood; all kinds of flavourings have been tried to disguise it, with little success.

External uses of the oil were also quite frequent in the past, for problems such as ringworm, abscesses, carbuncles, etc. It also has found a wide number of non-medicinal applications, for instance in manufacture of soaps, leather, dyes, varnishes and so on. Mrs Grieve quotes the *Chemist and Druggist* of 1922 giving a description of using the oil to clean paintings.

## CULTIVATION

The Castor Oil plant can be raised from seed, preferably with heat, and may need to be treated as an annual in England, except in warmer parts of the south,

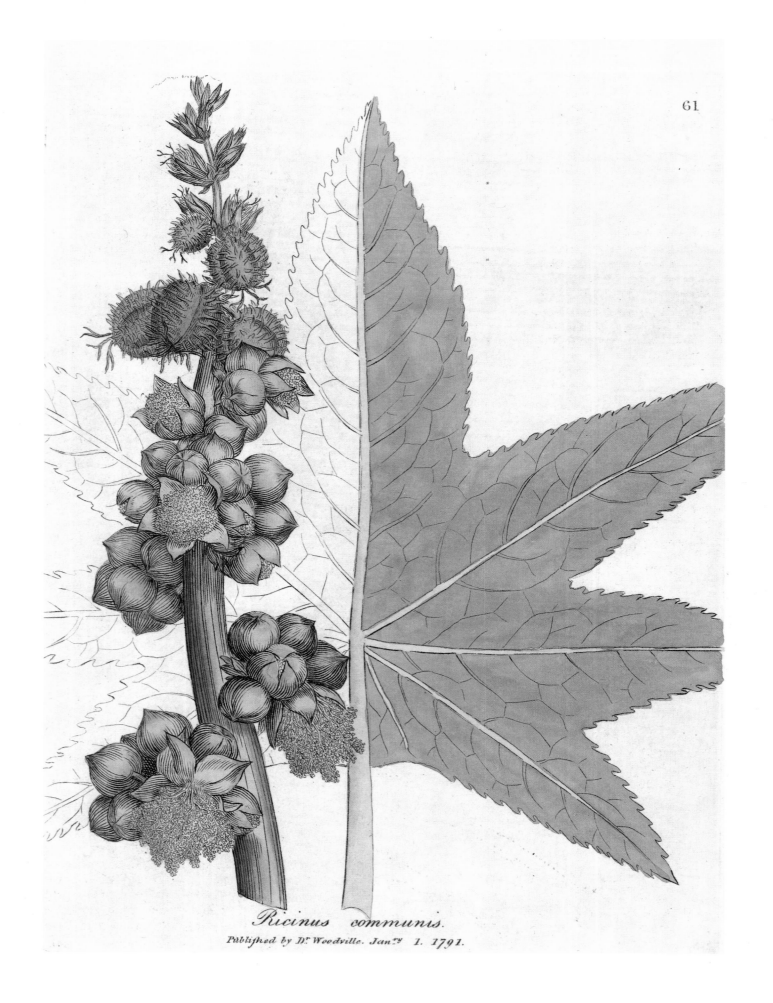

*Ricinus communis.*

Published by Dr. Woodville. Jan.ry 1. 1791.

although it has been known to grow as far north as Norway. It forms a handsome plant that has been popular for ornamental purposes, especially in Victorian times, when it would have been grown in hot-beds — thick piles of manure and straw that generated a great deal of warmth.

## MODERN MEDICINAL USES

Castor oil is no longer used by herbalists, who prefer safer and gentler laxatives where they are necessary. It has been part of conventional medicines, available from pharmacies, and is still at times used in Chinese medicine as a purgative. The seeds are highly poisonous, containing two toxic substances, ricin and ricinin, which do not pass into the oil.

Annual Capsicum *Capsicum annuum* from Woodville's *Medical Botany*, 1790.

Opposite: Castor Oil Plant *Ricinus communis* Woodville's *Medical Botany*, 1790.

Left: Palma Chrisi or Castor Oil Plant from Gerard's *Herball*.

# Cayenne

*Capsicum minimum*, Solanaceae

## DESCRIPTION

Cayenne is a well-known spice, either in the ground powder form or as the whole pods, when it is usually known as Chillies. It grows in most tropical and subtropical countries, from central America to Africa, India and the East Indies.

It is a shrubby plant, with angular, branching stems growing two or three feet high; they have a purplish tinge at the leaf nodes. The leaves are smooth and ovate in shape, and generally the plant shows that it is a member of the potato family. The long fruits are green when immature, slowly ripening to a bright red colour, and contain many flat, kidney-shaped seeds. The aroma and taste is highly pungent and unmistakable.

## HISTORY AND ORIGINS

Cayenne was actually introduced into Britain from India during the sixteenth century, and soon established itself in our *materia medica*. The name *capsicum* comes from the term 'to bite' and refers to its pungency.

Culpeper called it Guinea pepper, and describes the pods thus: "(they) are of a fiery, sharp, biting taste, and of a tem-

Pepper from *De Historia Stirpium* by Leonhart Fuchs, 1542.

Cayenne *Capsicum* Leonhart Fuchs's *De Historia Stirpium* 1542.

perature hot and dry". He nevertheless regards Cayenne highly, and says: "Put in the diet it drives away wind and helps flatulency, taken into a cold stomach with the meat, it gives great relief, causing phlegm to be voided; it helps digestion, gives appetite, provokes urine."

Although advised against for gastric inflammation, it has long been used to improve a flagging digestion. Mrs Grieve quotes a West Indian preparation called *Mandram*, for weak digestion, which is basically a kind of chutney with lots of Chillies mashed up in the liquid.

Cayenne was one of the central herbs in the North American tradition of herbal medicine, stemming from the ideas of Samuel Thomson; these in turn were a blend of Indian herbalism and early settlers' skills. One of the key elements in this system was the 'equalizing of heat' or improvement in circulation, and large doses of Cayenne were frequently employed for this. Thomson's ideas were developed in the nineteenth century into a philosophy called Physiomedicalism, which still has value for modern herbal medicine.

### CULTIVATION

While Cayenne grows happily in hot countries throughout the year, the seedpods often not ripening until November in India, for example, in Britain it needs to be treated as at best a half-hardy annual and nearly always as a greenhouse plant. The ground pepper is made from fully ripened fruits; the unripe pods have a somewhat bitter pungency.

### MODERN MEDICINAL USES

Cayenne is the strongest stimulant to the circulation in herbal medicine, both increasing the flow of blood and the sensation of warmth. It is therefore prescribed for conditions marked by cold or poor circulation; externally, it has been used as a rubefacient, or counter-irritant, for rheumatic disorders, and also for unbroken chilblains.

It is also useful for improving weak digestion, flatulence and colic, but should be avoided in heartburn or gastric acidity. Generally it is of great help for debilitated states.

*157*

*Chironia Centaurium*

Published by D.r Woodville August 1. 1792.

Common Centaury *Chironia centaurium* Woodville's *Medical Botany*, 1790.

# Centaury

*Centaurium erythraea*, Gentianaceae

### DESCRIPTION

Centaury is a native of Europe, North Africa and parts of Asia. It grows on dry banks and pastures or chalky cliffs, and varies considerably in size and overall appearance depending on location.

The upright stem branches out greatly at the top, the plant growing from a couple of inches to over a foot in height. The shiny, pale-green, ovate leaves form a tuft at the base, with more lanceolate leaves in pairs up the stem. They are topped with flat panicles of pink flowers, which only open in fine weather.

## HISTORY AND ORIGINS

The name Centaury derives from the Greek centaur Chiron, the mythical half-man, half-horse who was famous in legend for his skill with medicines. An old English name is Felwort, or gall plant, referring to its intense bitterness, and many writers speak of this property. Since all bitters have tonic and healing effects, it has also been called Feverwort for its benefits in febrile conditions. External applications were frequently given for wounds, sores and ulcerated injuries, again dating back to Chiron, who is supposed to have healed himself of a wound from a poisoned arrow.

Saxon herbalists used Centaury for such fevers, and like the ancient Gauls they gave it for bites or poisoning; since these were often seen as the result of evil influences, we find references to its value against "wykked sperytis" in the tenth century.

Culpeper praises it highly, saying it is "very wholesome, but not very toothsome". He recommends it, amongst other things, because it "openeth obstructions of the liver, gall, and spleen, helpeth the jaundice, and easeth the pains in the sides, and hardness of the spleen, used outwardly, and is given with very good effect in agues".

There was a famous old medicine for relieving the symptoms of gout called Portland Powder, which was based on Centaury. Culpeper too mentions this use, saying that it is "very effectual in all old pains of the joints, as the gout". This is probably due to its effects on the liver and kidneys.

Generally, most of its uses are associated with stimulating the liver and digestive system; it has been used as a substitute for quinine at times of scarcity, and for assisting other remedies for intestinal worms. Mrs Grieve said that "of all the bitter appetizing wild herbs which serve as excellent simple tonics, the Centaury is the most efficacious".

## CULTIVATION

Centaury is not at all easy to grow in gardens, needing a dry, rather poor soil, ideally on a chalky base, and it has mainly been collected from the wild.

## MODERN MEDICINAL USES

The bitter glycosides that Centaury contains make it one of the bitterest remedies available; this in the main gives it its actions, of improving digestion and liver function. It is valuable wherever there is a sluggish or debilitated digestion, or in mild fevers, and will act as a general tonic. It was a traditional spring tonic, and is prescribed in loss of appetite or even anorexia.

# Chamomile

*Chamaemelum nobile (Anthemis nobilis)*,
Compositae

## DESCRIPTION

Chamomiles are found growing widely throughout the temperate regions of the Northern hemisphere; they prefer dry soils and are common in fields and on wastelands and commons. The True Chamomile is a low-growing perennial, at most a foot high and sometimes trailing or creeping on the ground. By contrast, the wild Chamomile is an annual which can reach two feet in height.

The finely divided leaves give Chamomile a feathery appearance. The flowers are daisy-like in shape and colour, although the yellow centre is more conical — differences between species depend largely on small variations in the florets. For instance, the yellow centre, or receptacle, is solid in *Chamaemelum nobile* and hollow in *Matricaria chamomilla*.

The fresh herb exudes a strong, pleasant odour which is somewhat similar to that of apples. This similarity was noted long ago by the ancient Greeks, who called it *kamai* (on the ground) and *melon* (apple). In Spain it is still called *manzanilla*, or little apple, and it flavours a sherry of the same name.

## HISTORY AND ORIGINS

Chamomile has been the subject of some debate amongst botanists, who keep reclassifying it since there are a number of closely related species. Two have been

Chamomile from *Herbarium Vivae Eicones* by Otto Brunfels, 1537.

Opposite: Chamomile *Anthemis nobilis* Woodville's *Medical Botany*, 1790.

Pl.42.

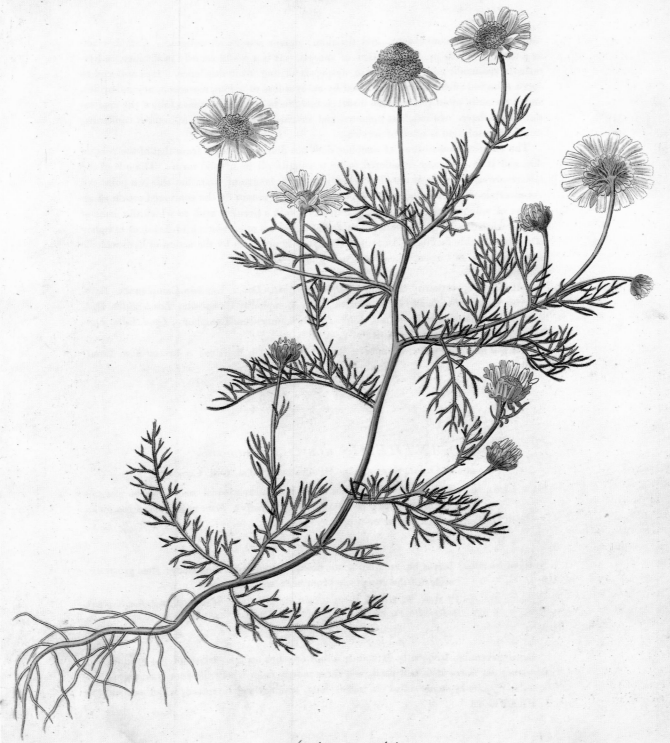

*Anthemis nobilis.*

W.E.Lizars sculpt.

used as medicines for many centuries: the wild or German Chamomile (*Matricaria chamomilla*), and the True or Roman Chamomile (*Chamaemelum nobile*). The latter was traditionally the favourite of the herbalists, especially a double-flowered variety which was highly popular by the sixteenth century, but the properties and uses of these species are very similar.

The True Chamomile has been grown as a form of lawn, and a non-flowering variety, Treneague, is nowadays most used for this, for instance at Buckingham Palace. Walking on the plants creates a wonderfully aromatic lawn; during the Middle Ages Chamomile was used as one of the strewing herbs to lay on the floors of houses for the same effect.

It features in all the old herbals, with long lists of complaints for which it is efficacious. Culpeper, for example, mentions that it "moderately comforteth all parts that have need of warmth, digesteth and dissolveth whatsoever hath need thereof . . . easeth all the pains of the colic and stone, and all pains and torment of the belly, and gently provoketh urine".

The reputation of Chamomile has remained high for many centuries, and it is a valuable remedy in professional herbal practice and popular in folk medicine to this day. It is frequently drunk instead of tea, especially on the Continent, and is given to children in commercial preparations of various kinds.

It also has a long tradition as a 'plant doctor', being grown at intervals throughout the garden to keep other plants healthy, and modern investigations confirm its beneficial properties in many instances; this kind of companion planting is making a comeback, particularly in organic gardening.

## CULTIVATION

Since it grows prolifically in the wild, Chamomile has few special requirements in terms of soil fertility. It prefers a sunny position, and thrives quite happily in dry, light soil. It is generally propagated by division and cuttings; the annual Chamomile will self-seed abundantly, or can be sown in mid-spring.

## MODERN MEDICINAL USES

The flowers have relaxant, anti-spasmodic and anti-inflammatory actions, and these, coupled with their bitter properties, which stimulate digestive functions, give them a wide range of applications. In addition, they are diuretic and help induce sweating. Chamomile may be considered the prime home remedy for minor digestive upsets, especially in children or if there is tension and restlessness. The azulene content of the volatile oil is very valuable as a wound-healer, and creams or ointments are employed to help a number of skin conditions. Herbalists may use it for these and other problems:

■ Irritable bowel, with colicky pains and looseness.
■ Painful periods with cramping pains.
■ Tension headaches, or headaches accompanying liverish upsets.
■ To relieve feverish colds and 'flu symptoms.
■ Externally, for irritated eyes in hay fever or mild conjunctivitis.
■ Cystitis, to increase urine flow and reduce inflammation.
■ Travel sickness or perhaps morning sickness.

## Chaste Berry

*Vitex agnus-castus*, Verbenaceae

### DESCRIPTION

The Chasteberry tree, a densely branched, deciduous shrub, is indigenous to the countries around the Mediterranean and spreading into Asia. It grows to around fifteen feet, with linear, lanceolate leaves, divided into several leaflets. The leaves are covered on the underside, as are the young shoots, with a fine grey down.

The violet, fragrant flowers appear in whorls on long terminal racemes, in September. These are followed by the berries, which resemble peppercorns, of a dark-purple colour when ripe and slightly aromatic.

The Chaste Tree from Gerard's *Herball*.

222

*Vitex Agnus castus*

Published by D.r Woodville March A. 1794.

Chaste Berry *Vitex agnus-castux* Woodville's *Medical Botany*, 1790.

At times it has been mentioned as an aphrodisiac, and at others as an anaphrodisiac! This contradiction, and its reputation for inducing chastity, revolve around the effects of Chaste Berry on the pituitary gland, and consequently on progesterone production. Since this is something that only modern research has been able to establish, the plant is much more widely used today than in the past, with better-defined areas of use. In Mrs Grieve's day, she recommends it simply for the relief of pain and weakness in the limbs, with no reference to menstrual or hormonal problems.

## CULTIVATION

The Chaste Tree is a shrub of much warmer climates than that of Britain, and it is unlikely to be successfully cultivated in this country, and certainly not to the extent of obtaining fruits, which only ripen in October or November.

## MODERN MEDICINAL USES

Medical herbalists make great use of the Chaste Berry nowadays. Its effects on the anterior pituitary are essentially balancing, but it thus encourages the production of the luteotrophic hormone. This in turn improves the function of the corpus luteum, the body that is left behind in the ovary when ovulation has taken place. This chiefly promotes progesterone production during the second half of the menstrual cycle, and a prime indication for prescribing Chaste Berry are problems associated with the premenstrual syndrome.

Chaste Berry may also be given to some women having difficulties during the menopause, also to breast-feeding mothers where there is inadequate milk production; it may be helpful for some women suffering from the 'baby blues', the depression that is partly due to the drop in hormone levels a little while after childbirth. Naturally, the precise prescription will be an individual thing, depending on the whole circumstances for each person.

Another use of Chaste Berry can be to help women to regain hormonal balance and control after a time of being on the contraceptive pill.

## HISTORY AND ORIGINS

As the name suggests, the berries from this shrub have been held in high repute for preserving chastity, and the ancient Greeks used to honour them especially. They feature in the rites of Ceres, and as potions for the priestesses.

There is surprisingly little about them in the old literature, perhaps because most of the medicinal attention was on increasing fertility. In Chinese medicine, a related species, *Vitex trifolia*, has been used over the centuries as an analgesic and sedative, although it is phrased differently in their medical terms.

# Cleavers

*Galium aparine*, Rubiaceae

269

## DESCRIPTION

Cleavers, sometimes called Clivers, or Goosegrass, is a weak climbing annual that is found in hedgerows and waste ground throughout Europe and the eastern side of North America. The family to which it belongs is a very large one, including some highly useful tropical plants, most notably coffee.

Cleavers, like other related plants found in Britain, is much smaller than some of these exotica; it has slim, angular stems that straggle their way through and over other plants. The narrow, lanceolate leaves are arranged in whorls up the stem, and both leaves and stems are covered with tiny hooked bristles, which cling on to plants, animals and clothing, as countless children have found out!

The flowers are quite insignificant, greenish-white in colour. They give way to the small, globular fruit. These too are covered with bristles, and by clinging to sheep or other animals they get dispersed. Some of its ancient nicknames derive from the term for robber, as it plucks at the sheep's wool.

## HISTORY AND ORIGINS

As mentioned, most of its old names refer to its clinging habit. The name Goosegrass could be due to the fact that geese and ducks, like many animals, will eat it very happily. The distant relationship with coffee can be seen in the tradition in parts of Scandinavia of drying and roasting the fruits as a coffee substitute.

Cleavers was known and used by the Greeks and Romans, and for many centuries since, as a cleanser for the blood and mild diuretic. The old Physicians of Myddfai listed many ailments for which it was to be taken, recommending the juice of the plant to be taken through the spring, to "expel and completely destroy eruptive poison from the blood". By doing so, they felt it might help clear up such problems as "eruptions, boils, scalds, scrophula, lepra, cancer, ery-

*Galium Aparine*

Published by D.r Woodville, Dec.r 1. 1794.

Cleavers *Galium aparine* Woodville's *Medical Botany*, 1790.

Goose-grass or Cleavers form Gerard's *Herball*.

sipelas, pneumonia, dropsy, rheumatism, gout, strangury" and many more — an impressive list!

Culpeper is a little more restrained, simply advising it as a spring cleanser and tonic. Its diuretic effect is seen in his suggestion that "it is familiarly taken in broth, to keep them lean and lank that are apt to grow fat". Pliny, writing over fifteen hundred years before, says something very similar.

External preparations of Cleavers, such as ointments, are quite commonly found in old herbals, for wounds and ulcers. It acquired a particular reputation for skin tumours, both as a local application and the juice taken internally as an alterative, or blood-cleanser.

## CULTIVATION

The best way to have this plant in the garden is to have a neglected corner, perhaps by a hedge, where it can have its head and spread unchecked! Most people probably regard it as a trouble-some weed, so cultivation is not really needed. The fresh plant, gathered and made into a tea, tastes a little like the water used for cooking peas, and gathering it from the wild will in most cases be the best method.

## MODERN MEDICINAL USES

Cleavers is a diuretic, stimulating the passing of urine, and is often given in conditions of fluid retention, poor lymph drainage, urinary infections and so on. It has a particular effect on the lymphatic system, encouraging it to work more effectively, and may be prescribed in many infections where the lymph glands are raised.

# Coltsfoot

*Tussilago farfara*, Compositae

## DESCRIPTION

Coltsfoot is widely distributed throughout Britain and Europe, even extending into northern Africa and parts of Asia, and less widely in the United States. It especially likes heavy, clay soils and can be quite prolific in ditches and by river banks.

An old name for Coltsfoot was *filius ante patrem*, the son before the father, because the bright-yellow flowers appear from February to March, before the leaves. The dandelion-like flowers are supported on a distinctive hairy stem. As the flowers turn to downy clocks of seed, the large leaves develop. These are hoof-shaped, hence the name, and the under-surface stays covered with loose, white woolly hairs.

The small, white creeping rootstock can lie dormant for long periods, springing up if the ground is disturbed. Once in a garden, it can be difficult to eradicate.

## HISTORY AND ORIGINS

Coltsfoot has been considered for centuries to be one of the most popular cough remedies; indeed its Latin name *Tussilago* means 'cough dispeller'. All the ancient writers from Dioscorides to Galen and Pliny recommended smoking the leaves for a cough; for instance, Pliny advised that the dried leaves were burnt on charcoal and the smoke taken into the mouth through a hollow reed. It has been for many years the main ingredient of the British Herb Tobacco, and can be bought in this form today.

Different countries have recommended the leaves, roots or flowers for making cough remedies. In France, the flowers used to be painted on to the door-posts of apothecaries' shops to indicate the business of the premises. The flowers in particular were used to make a syrup, listed in various editions of the *British Pharmacopeia*.

Gerard wrote of Coltsfoot: "A decoction of the greene leaves and roots, or else a syrup thereof, is good for the cough that proceedeth of a thin rheume." Similarly, Culpeper praised it highly: "The fresh leaves, or juice, or syrup thereof, is good for a hot, dry cough, or wheezing, and shortness of breath." They too point out its value when

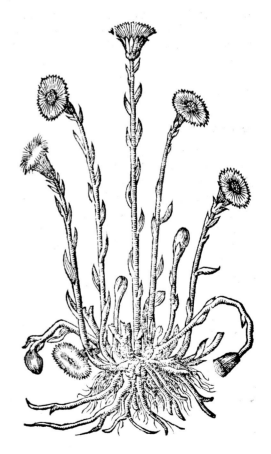

Coltsfoot in flower from Gerard's *Herball*.

*13*

Coltsfoot *Tussilago farfara* Woodville's *Medical Botany*, 1790.

smoked, either breathed through a funnel or taken like tobacco.

Folk medicine tended simply to use a tea, or tisane, to loosen the cough, or else people would visit the apothecary to buy Coltsfoot Rock to chew. A glass or two of home-made Coltsfoot wine was probably the most pleasant way of relieving a cough.

External uses of Coltsfoot also seem to have been popular in times past. Gerard recommends pounding the fresh leaves with honey to apply to hot swellings and inflammations, while Culpeper prefers to use distilled water from the plant for the same purposes. The Physicians of Mydd-fai suggest boiling the leaves in cow's milk with "oaten groats and May butter, and apply warm to the painful part".

Other old uses for the plant included the tradition in some parts of Scotland of

stuffing pillows with the downy seed-heads, a practice similar to some birds who line their nests with these silky hairs. The hairs on the leaves were occasionally collected and dried for use as tinder before matches were created.

## CULTIVATION

Coltsfoot can easily become an invasive weed, and buying a single plant can produce enough offspring to satisfy most herb gardeners. Keep it to a waste area, preferably though not necessarily in a dampish, heavy soil. The flower-stalks are collected in February, the leaves not until June.

## MODERN MEDICINAL USES

The mucilage content of the plant make it very soothing for an inflamed respiratory tract, and the traditional uses in loosening a harsh, dry, spasmodic cough are confirmed by clinical practice today. Where there is an irritable element in the cough, for instance in asthma, then the herb is very helpful indeed.

The leaves have been found to be quite rich in zinc, and this may explain its anti-inflammatory action, both internally for bronchial disorders and externally as a poultice or compress for problems such as boils or abscesses.

# *Comfrey*

*Symphytum officinale*, Boraginaceae

## DESCRIPTION

Comfrey is a common weed of Britain, Europe, America and temperate parts of Asia. It is especially prolific on heavy, clay soils, and on the banks of rivers, canals and ditches. It grows vigorously, with long lanceolate leaves spreading out from a central rosette. The leaves are decurrent, that is partly extending down

Opposite: Comfrey from Mrs Loudon's *The Ladies' Flower-Garden of Ornamental Perennials* Vol. II, 1843–44. 1. *Cynoglossum omphaloides* 2. *C. pictum* 3. *Symphytum officinale* 4. *S. caucasicum* 5. *S. asperimum* 6. *Osnoma taurica*.

Pl. 77.

the stem beyond the point of attachment.

The plant grows to some three feet, and the leaves are characteristically hairy and rough to the touch. They are topped by one-sided clusters of drooping, bell-shaped flowers, which vary in colour from creamy-white to pink or purple. The roots are much branched and quite thick in size, blackish on the outside and white and fleshy inside.

### HISTORY AND ORIGINS

The reputation of Comfrey as a wound herb, to heal injuries and even fractures, is one that extends back many centuries. Both the English and Latin names refer to the property of uniting or mending, and many country titles such as Knitbone attest to its virtues.

In medieval times it enjoyed an especially high reputation; Baker, in *Jewell of Health* (1567), says: "The water of the Greater Comferie druncke helpeth such as are bursten, and that have broken the bone of the legge." As might be expected, Culpeper is very knowledgeable about the plant, and makes these recommendations, among others: "The root boiled in water or wine, and the decoction drank, helps all inward hurts, bruises, wounds, and ulcers of the lungs, and causes the phlegm that oppresses him to be easily spit forth ... a syrup made thereof is very effectual for all those inward griefs and hurts ... and for outward wounds or sores in the fleshy or sinewy part of the body ... The roots being outwardly applied, help fresh wounds or cuts immediately, being bruised and laid thereto: and is special good for ruptures and broken bones."

All these writers noted that Comfrey was rich in "slimie substance", as Gerard called it, and this mucilage was and is valuable in soothing preparations. By the beginnings of this century, analysis of Comfrey had shown it to contain a substance called allantoin, which acts as a cell-proliferant to speed up healing. Writers in the *British Medical Journal* at the time noted the benefits of this compound, both internally and externally, and Mrs Grieve quotes the *Chemist and Druggist* from 1921: "Allantoin is a fresh instance of the good judgement of our rustics, especially of old times, with

Comfrey *Symphytum officinale* Woodville's *Medical Botany*, 1790.

regard to the virtues of plants."

Apart from its medicinal uses, Comfrey has been eaten as a vegetable, mainly by vegans due to its Vitamin B12 content. The young leaves are cooked like spinach. In the past, the roots have been roasted as ingredients in coffee substitutes, although Dandelion roots are more commonly used nowadays.

### CULTIVATION

Comfrey does best in moisture-retentive soil, preferably with some shade. Propagation can be from seed or by division of the roots in the autumn. Even tiny pieces of root are capable of producing new plants, so eradication is often harder than cultivation. Give at least two feet each way between plants.

## MODERN MEDICINAL USES

Comfrey is an excellent healing agent, and is incorporated into creams, ointments and so on for cuts, grazes, wounds and even ulcers. Internally it is also very valuable for gastric inflammation or ulceration. The very high mucilage content combines with the healing properties of allantoin and the astringency of tannins for the overall effect.

The other main area of action is as a relaxing expectorant, where it helps both to soothe the inflamed membranes and ease the expulsion of phlegm. There have been a few doubts raised over its safety internally in long-term high dosage, although these have not been substantiated despite some press reports. There are no reports of problems from clinical use, and external use, need not cause any anxiety at all.

# Coriander

*Coriandrum sativum*, Umbelliferae

## DESCRIPTION

Coriander is now widespread through many parts of of the world, from China, Japan and Indo-China through India and the Mediterranean to South America. Occasionally it can be found in Britain on wasteland or by rivers.

It is an upright annual, growing to around three feet or less. The lower leaves are pinnate in shape, with oval leaflets, while the upper leaves are more finely cut and divided. The flower umbels are held on short stalks, and are white and dainty. The fruits are globular, turning from green to ash-brown when ripe, when they drop very quickly.

The bright-green leaves in particular have a very pungent and distinctive smell; the name Coriander is considered to be derived from the Greek *koros*, a bug, in reference to this long-lasting aroma. The seeds share this scent to a lesser extent, but become much more fragrantly aromatic when dried.

## HISTORY AND ORIGINS

As an aromatic spice and culinary herb, Coriander has been held in high esteem since the earliest civilizations. The finest plants were considered to have been grown in Egypt in ancient times, and its uses spread to the Greeks and Romans. In Middle Eastern cookery today Coriander is still a vital ingredient, both the seeds and the fresh leaves. In American

Coriander *Coriandrum sativum* from *Getreue Darstellung…Arzneykunde…*, F.G. Haynes 1821.

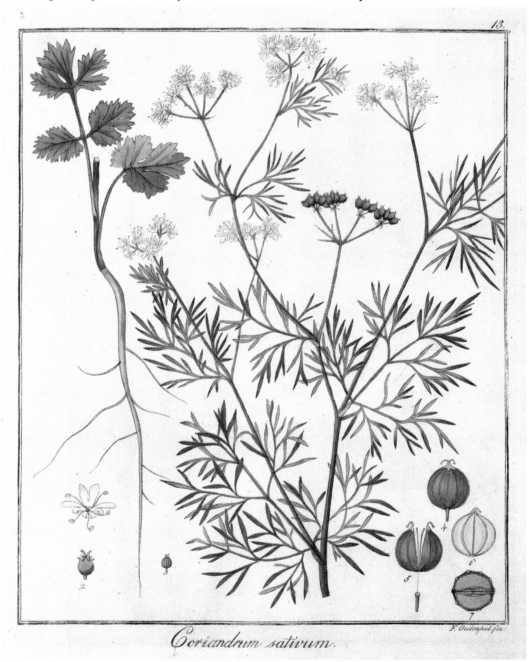

*Coriandrum sativum.*

countries like Peru this habit of including large quantities of leaves in dishes is also a long tradition — it can be overwhelming in taste and odour to Western palates!

The seeds are much more widely used in Europe, although sometimes only as a part of a curry powder, but in the past they were mixed into dough for bread. Another old method of using them was in the form of small comfits, or sugar sweets. To this day they are included in recipes for alcoholic spirits, notably in gin, with juniper and other spices.

Medicinally, all the countries that have

used them have agreed on their value as a carminative, to get rid of wind and colicky pains. For a long time they were official in the *British Pharmacopoeia* as a vehicle to disguise unpleasant medicines, and to ease the griping of strong purgative medications such as senna. In China they were thought to confer immortality, although excessive amounts are almost narcotic in their effects, but they are still officially used as stomachic medicines.

In the West, medicinal usefulness dates right back to Hippocrates. Mention of it can be found in the writings of many physicians, from Pliny through to medieval times. For instance, Turner writes: "Coriandre layd to wyth breade or barly mele is good for Saynt Antonyes fyre." Coriander water was an old favourite for infantile colic, much as Dill water was and still is very popular.

## CULTIVATION

Coriander likes to have a sunny, warm soil. It does best on light soils, although it has been successfully grown, and lived as an escape, on the heavier clays of East Anglia and Essex. The seeds should be sown in April, or earlier, in heat as they take quite a while to germinate. The new plants' seed-heads ripen in August or early September, and the seeds can be easily shaken off.

## MODERN MEDICINAL USES

Like many aromatic seeds, Coriander is a very useful carminative, and may be prescribed wherever there is flatulence, griping or colic. It is less frequently used nowadays in herbal medicine, but may be suggested in the diet to aid other medication. The aromatic volatile oil acts as a stimulant to the stomach, improving the appetite and digestion.

# Cowslip

*Primula veris*, Primulaceae

## DESCRIPTION

Very closely related to both the Primrose and the Oxlip, the Cowslip is found in grassland in Britain, Europe and temper-

*Primula veris*

Cowslip *Primula veris* from *Getreue Darstellung…Arzneykunde*, F.G. Haynes 1813.

ate regions of Asia. It is a perennial, the leaves appearing in early spring, initially as tightly-coiled little balls which unfold into a rosette of oblong, toothed leaves, slightly fatter and shorter than those of the Primrose.

From the centre of this rosette rises the flower stalk, and the flowers themselves are held on separate little stalks, in an umbel shape. They are cup-shaped and slightly brighter yellow than a Primrose, and each petal is marked with a small red spot. The flowers have an unusual and distinctive aroma.

## HISTORY AND ORIGINS

Cowslips have been given many country names over the centuries, several of them

Cowslip from *Commentarii in Sex Libros Pedacii Dioscoridis* by Pierandrea Matthioli, 1565.

being variations on the name 'Keyflower'. This refers to the shape of the flower-heads, which were thought to resemble a bunch of keys; the flowers were originally dedicated in Norse mythology to Freya, who carried the keys to her treasure palace. With advancing Christianity, this became 'Our Lady's Keys' or else perhaps 'Herb Peter'.

For a long time Cowslips were a very popular home remedy, especially for inducing restfulness and sleep, and easing migrainous headaches. Culpeper writes: "Because they strengthen the brain and nerves, and remedy palsies, the Greeks gave them the name paralysis". Gerard advised: "The roots of Primrose [Cowslips and Primroses were used identically] stamped and strained, and the juice sniffed into the nose with a quill or such like, purgeth the brain, and qualifieth the pain of the megrim."

The most popular way of taking Cowslips was as Cowslip wine, and each village had their own recipe for this; sadly, this probably was the main reason for the decline in numbers of the plants in pasture land, hastened later on by farming methods. In Medieval times they were so plentiful that apothecaries' shops sold them by the tub. Today they are

making a slow recovery in Britain, and can still be bought in wine-making shops. Since the tea does not have a very special taste, the wine is the most pleasant way to take Cowslips!

Another quite different traditional use for Cowslips was to improve the complexion, and there are many old recipes for ointments. Culpeper suggests using the leaves pounded together with hog's grease, although the flowers were better still, and such an ointment "taketh away spots and wrinkles of the skin, sunburnings and freckles, and adds beauty exceedingly". This value as a skin clearer was considered almost magical, and Shakespeare refers to this in his most herb lore-rich play, *A Midsummer Night's Dream*:

In their gold coats spots you see,
These be rubies fairy favours
In those freckles lie their savours.

## CULTIVATION

Because Cowslips have declined so much in this country, growing them is essential to preserve the wild stocks. The seeds can be bought from several wild-flower specialists, and also seeds collected from existing garden plants may be sown as soon as they are ripe — leaf-mould can be used instead of potting compost. The plants can also be successfully propagated by dividing the roots in autumn.

## MODERN MEDICINAL USES

The flowers have anti-spasmodic and sedative properties, and are very valuable for insomnia or headaches due to nervousness and anxiety. They are also expectorant, and are sometimes prescribed in bronchitic conditions, to increase the removal of phlegm; at the same time they will reduce restlessness, for instance in children with whooping cough. The flowers contain small amounts of salicylates, which probably accounts for some traditional mentions of its uses in rheumatic conditions, although it is not generally given for these problems nowadays.

# Dandelion

*Taraxacum officinale*, Compositae

## DESCRIPTION

This plant is so well known it is hardly worth describing; it grows prolifically all over the northern hemisphere, originally coming from central Asia. It prefers moist ground, but will grow virtually anywhere, as farmers and gardeners know very well!

The characteristically indented leaves, which give rise to the name (a corruption of the French *dent de lion*), grow in a rosette at the base of the plant. The hollow stem rises from the centre of this rosette, and the leaves are so grooved that rainfall is conducted to the middle of the rosette, and so down to the root.

The yellow flower-heads turn eventually to a 'clock' of seeds, familiar to all children for various games. All the parts exude a milky-white sap when cut, es-

Dandelion from Gerard's *Herball*.

Pl. 9.

*Leontodon Taraxacum*

W.H.Lizars sculp.

pecially the stem and root. The thick tap root can penetrate deep into the earth, and this is one of the reasons why they are so difficult to control or eradicate.

### HISTORY AND ORIGINS

Dandelions seem to have been first mentioned by Arab physicians in the tenth century, the roots being used for digestive and liver complaints. The old Welsh physicians also wrote of its uses for jaundice and the like. Mostly the roots were employed, and references to Dandelion juice and extracts appear throughout Europe and as far as India. The dried root was an official preparation in the *US Pharmacopoeia*.

Medieval herbalists took up the medicinal benefits of Dandelion with enthusiasm; Culpeper says it is "very effectual for the obstructions of the liver, the jaundice and the hypochondriac; it openeth the passages of the urine both in young and old", and he notes the custom on the Continent of eating the leaves in spring, with the wry comment, "you may see plainly without a pair of spectacles, that foreign physicians are not so selfish as ours are, but more communicative of the virtues of plants to people".

By his day, herbalists had already begun to recognize that the leaves and root had slightly differing actions, the former being a good diuretic. This has led to many folk-names for the plant, such as 'piss-en-lit' or 'piss-a-beds', and the saying, "pick a dandelion and wet the bed".

Various drinks have been made from the Dandelion; a coffee substitute is made by roasting the roots, and this is now quite popular again as concern grows about consumption of caffeine. In the past the ground root might have been mixed with chocolate, which was perhaps less healthy! Dandelion beer, from the leaves, was frequently brewed both in England and in North America, especially Canada. The flowers make a delicious wine, which was taken as a tonic.

The young leaves have traditionally been used as a vegetable, either as a spring salad or cooked like spinach. In his *Acetaria*, John Evelyn says: "With this homely salley, Hecate entertained Theseus."

Dandelion can be useful in the garden too, providing nectar for the bees from early spring, when supplies are scarce, to late autumn. Mrs Grieve reports that "no less than ninety-three different kinds of insects are in the habit of frequenting it".

### CULTIVATION

The plants can be grown in any odd corner of the garden, even in shade, if there are not enough growing naturally. Some people use forcing pots to blanch the leaves and reduce the bitterness, although this is an essential part of the action as a digestive tonic. Keeping the plants in check is likely to be more necessary; one way of doing this is to keep pinching out the flower-heads or clocks if they appear. There are French and Italian varieties with larger, more succulent leaves for salad use.

### MODERN MEDICINAL USES

Dandelions contain bitter glycosides amongst other chemicals, which are important in the plant's actions as a liver and digestive tonic. It is also quite rich in several vitamins and minerals, and the leaves in particular are rich in potassium. Since an increase in urine flow leads naturally to an increased loss of potassium, Dandelion can be seen to be a very useful remedy in maintaining this balance. The leaves may thus be prescribed where there is oedema.

The roots are primarily employed medicinally for indigestion with mild constipation, poor liver and gall-bladder function, and thus for symptoms of toxin build-up, such as skin conditions and rheumatic disorders. The liver is considered in herbal medicine to be uniquely under stress, from dietary, environmental and chemical factors, so Dandelions are a valuable part of many treatments.

The fresh sap, especially from the stem, can be of use as a local application for warts, taking care to avoid getting the juice in the eyes.

# Elder

*Sambucus nigra*, Caprifoliaceae

### DESCRIPTION

The Elder is a shrubby tree that appears in hedgerows, woods and wastelands throughout Europe, America and Asia, often being grown in gardens. It is described well by Mrs Grieve, who says: "The elder, with its flat-topped masses of creamy-white fragrant blossoms, followed by large drooping bunches of purplish-black, juicy berries, is a familiar object in English countryside and gardens."

The stiff stems contain a soft pith that is easily pushed out, something which countless children have exploited over the centuries to make a pop-gun, or a whistle. The leaves are pinnate, with an odd leaflet at the end, and the flowers grow in flat umbels. They give out a heavy scent in the summer. The tree can grow to as high as thirty feet.

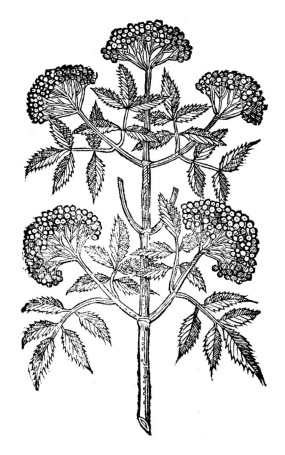

The Common Elder Tree from Gerard's *Herball*.

Opposite: Dandelion *Taraxacum officinale* Woodville's *Medical Botany*, 1790.

HISTORY AND ORIGINS

The Elder tree has been the object of a tremendous amount of folk-lore and romantic beliefs for centuries, as well as being famous for its medicinal properties since the time of Hippocrates. The legends concerning the tree probably date back to pagan prehistory, but many of them have been founded on the belief that Judas Iscariot hanged himself on an Elder. For instance, in Langland's fourteenth-century work, *The Vision of Piers Plowman*, he writes:

Judas he japed with Jewen silver
And sithen an eller hanged hymselve.

Perhaps due to this belief, and also that the Holy Cross was made from elderwood, the tree was believed to ward off evil spirits. This belief can be found in many countries, from Britain to Russia, and led to the Elder being an emblem of death and sorrow, and connected with magic.

On a more practical level, the wood of old Elder trees is hard and with a fine, close grain, and has been used over the centuries for a variety of wooden instruments or artefacts. It was an important hedge-making wood too, an old tradition stating that a stake of Elder will last longer in the ground than an iron bar of the same dimensions.

At one time, the tree was an important source of vegetable dyes, the bark and root yielding a black dye, the leaves a green dye when fixed with alum, and the berries giving differing shades of violet depending on the fixative.

Both the flowers and the berries have been the source of homemade drinks and cordials for many years, and they are still very popular now. Elderflower syrup, cordial or sparkling wine, and elderberry 'rob', or wine, are some of the ways the plant is taken, both for pleasure and for its medicinal benefits.

The Elder has been praised as a medicine by all the writers, from Dioscorides and Pliny to the present day. It has been called the medicine chest of the country people, and it was said that the famous physician Boerhaave never passed an Elder without raising his hat to it as a mark of respect. We find in 1644 a whole

Common Elder *Sambucus ebulus* Woodville's *Medical Botany*, 1790.

book devoted to it, *The Anatomie of the Elder* by Dr Blockwich, which describes the properties of all parts of the tree.

The bark, and indeed the root, were employed as strong laxatives and diuretics, although this use is now obsolete, as is the use of the leaves to make an ointment for bruises, sprains, etc.

Culpeper describes the root thus: "The juice of the root taken, mightily procures vomitings, and purges the watery humours of the dropsy."

The flowers are the main parts which are still used medicinally, and for a long time Elderflower Water was listed in the *British Pharmacopoeia*, as a vehicle for eye and skin lotions. It was an important household preparation for keeping the skin clear and free from blemishes. Culpeper again: "The distilled water of the flowers is of much use to clean the skin from sun-burning, freckles, morphew, or the like."

## CULTIVATION

Elder trees prefer a rather damp soil, although they are likely to develop best in a fairly sunny site. They can be propagated by cuttings in autumn, and should be pruned in late autumn or very early spring. They are usually very hardy. Birds eat the berries frequently, and this helps to spread the seeds.

## MODERN MEDICINAL USES

The flowers have a powerful diaphoretic effect in the feverish patient, inducing sweating and regulating the temperature. They are also somewhat diuretic and expectorant, and are used in febrile conditions such as colds or influenza, and in catarrhal problems generally. They are often recommended as a hot infusion, to increase the sweating effect.

# Elecampane

*Inula helenium*, Compositae

## DESCRIPTION

Elecampane is found wild throughout southern Europe, and eastwards into Asia as far as the north-west of India; from long cultivation it is also found as a naturalized escape in parts of Britain and the USA. It is a tall and handsome plant, mainly found in wet pastures, or as Culpeper says, "in moist grounds and shadowy places".

The stiff, upright stems grow up to five feet or more, and are quite thick and furrowed. They branch at the top, and like the rest of the plant are covered in coarse hairs. The rough basal leaves are ovate and can be as much as eighteen inches long; the leaves higher up the stems are shorter and more rounded.

Elecampe from Gerard's *Herball*.

The large yellow flowers bloom from mid- to late summer, and resemble double sunflowers. They are followed by rectangular fruits, with a crown of reddish hairs. The medicinal parts are the roots, which are large and fleshy, with a pleasant aroma.

## HISTORY AND ORIGINS

Elecampane has been described for its medicinal virtues from Classical times, with all the ancient writers mentioning it, both for medicine and as a food. Pliny mentions how valued it was by many Romans, who would "let no day pass without eating some of the roots of *Enula*, considered to help digestion and cause mirth". The Latin name of *Inula* seems to be a corruption of *Helenion*, and there are many stories of its origin in the legends of Helen of Troy.

The tradition of using sugared cakes of Elecampane as sweetmeats continued right up until the last century, and it was considered useful for the stomach as well as the lungs. As a condiment, it probably helped when people had overeaten; this was certainly true of the Romans, who used it as a vegetable to recover from their enormous feasts!

The main area of use was for coughs and bronchial conditions, and researchers dating back to the seventeenth century have noted some its constituents. The most abundant of these is Inulin, a substance resembling starch, but probably the most significant is Helenin, a crystallizable compound including camphor that was isolated quite early on. This is a powerful bactericide, and in times past it was used in cases of tuberculosis.

Frequent mention of Elecampane as a bronchial remedy appears in Anglo-Saxon works, such as the Leech *Book of Bald*, and it was popular with the thirteenth-century Welsh Physicians of Myddfai, who wrote this recipe, among others: "Take the root of elecampane, two pennyworth of black pepper, and the same of the roots of mallows. Let them be powdered and made into a confection with clarified honey. Take as much as a pigeon's egg the first thing in the morning and the last at night."

Culpeper was well acquainted with Elecampane, calling it "one of the most beneficial roots nature affords for the help of the consumptive", and saying that "it has not its equal in the cure of the hooping-cough in children, when all other medicines fail". He recommended a syrup of the roots, both for coughs and wheezing, and also for improving digestion. Gerard also praised it, stating: "It is good for shortnesse of breathe and an old cough, and for such as cannot breathe unless they hold their neckes upright."

## CULTIVATION

Elecampane is fairly easily grown from seed, but is probably best cultivated by propagating from the roots in the autumn. It likes moist, good loam with reasonable drainage, and also does best in partial shade. Due to its potential size it needs a fair amount of room; allow a foot each way for each plant when growing. After a couple of years the roots will be ready to dig.

### MODERN MEDICINAL USES

As a bactericidal expectorant, Elecampane is very valuable in bronchial coughs, when there is a lot of congestion, stimulating the removal of the excess phlegm. It contains amounts of mucilage which have an accompanying soothing action — properties especially valuable for chesty coughs in older people, when they have difficulty in clearing the airways, or perhaps for young children with similar difficulties. Elecampane is additionally a warming digestive tonic, and is helpful in prescriptions for flatulence and poor digestion aggravated by the cold.

# Evening Primrose

*Oenothera biennis*, Onagraceae

### DESCRIPTION

Evening Primrose is a native of North America, but has been carried into Europe, growing wild in many countries. As its Latin name suggests, it is a biennial, with a fibrous, yellowish rootstock. During the first year a flat arrangement of leaves is produced, and from this the flowering stems rise in the second year to a height of four feet or more.

The leaves are pointed, and up to five inches long; like the stems they are covered with short hairs. The large, yellow flowers grow all along the stalks, and bloom in succession from June until October. They usually open in the early evening, hence the name, and give off a delicate aroma.

### HISTORY AND ORIGINS

Evening Primrose is unusual among medicinal plants, in that it has very little historical usage, but its modern reputation is largely the result of recent research. None of the older writers mention it in any detail, and even as late as the beginning of this century Mrs Grieve was writing that it was not much used. In her day, the bark and/or leaves were the parts used, infrequently, mainly for diarrhoea and dyspepsia. She also mentions that the roots have been used on the Continent as a salad garnish.

### CULTIVATION

The Evening Primrose is an adaptable and hardy plant that will thrive in many types of soil or position. Indeed, it has been considered a nuisance, especially in America, since it crops up all over the place. It perhaps does best in a warm, sunny site and with good drainage, say a sandy soil.

The seeds should be sown in April, and transplanted into a sunny spot. In the autumn, or the following spring, it can be moved again to its intended flowering position, although it has deep roots and care should be taken on moving it. If allowed to self-sow you will probably always have plants in the garden!

### MODERN MEDICINAL USES

The seeds of Evening Primrose contain an oil which modern research has shown to be very useful. This oil is rich in a substance called gamma-linoleic acid, or GLA, and this compound is a vital link in a number of chemical processes in the body.

It seems that some people are unable to produce GLA satisfactorily, and it is prescribed in a variety of situations. Menopausal changes, and also premenstrual problems, can sometimes be relieved by taking capsules of Oil of Evening Primrose. External use of the oil for eczema has now become an accepted form of treatment, available on prescription.

Oil of Evening Primrose is sometimes recommended to help with arthritic conditions, and an area which has attracted interest is its possible benefits in slowing down degenerative changes in multiple sclerosis. Whilst the number of complaints for which manufacturers of the oil recommend its use is perhaps overoptimistic, it does represent an exciting new addition to plant medicine.

# Eyebright

*Euphrasia officinalis*, Scrophulariaceae

### DESCRIPTION

A number of very closely related species, or varieties of the same species, are found widely distributed throughout Europe, Asia and North America. Eyebright takes a very variable appearance, but is generally no more than eight or nine inches in height.

It occurs naturally in grassland, heath and alpine pastures. It is bushy in shape, with small, deeply-cut leaves, sometimes rounded or else quite narrow. The little flowers are in loose spikes, and vary in colour from white, through pinky-red or even purple, sometimes with a definite yellow coloration. Eyebright is in the

Eyebright from Gerard's *Herball*.

Opposite: Evening Primrose *Oenothera biennis* from *Flora Danica*, G. Oeder 1770.

Eyebright *Euphrasia officinalis* Woodville's *Medical Botany*, 1790.

same family as the Foxglove, and the flowers bear a resemblance to these, although they are much smaller.

### History and Origins

The name *Euphrasia* derives from *Euphrosyne*, or gladness, which was also the name of one of the three Graces. This derivation is because of the properties that Eyebright has as a remedy for eye problems, hence the common name, which can thus cheer up people suffering from such troubles. A legend says that the linnet, which carries the same Greek name, first used Eyebright to clean its eyes and that of its young, and the bird then passed on this knowledge to mankind.

Surprisingly, there is little mention of Eyebright by ancient Greek writers, and it is not until the Middle Ages that references to it are common. It is first described as an external remedy for the eyes in the thirteenth century, and by Elizabethan times it was well established as a specific for such conditions across Europe. It came to be one of the examples of the 'Doctrine of Signatures', a belief which sprang up in medieval times that plants were signed in some way by God to indicate their medicinal properties. The spots and striations on the flowers looked somewhat like bloodshot eyes, and were therefore 'signed' for use in this type of problem.

In Tudor times, there was an ale flavoured with Eyebright that was quite popular, and we also find references to wine; Markham wrote in 1616, "Drinke everie morning a small draught of Eyebright wine." Gerard gives specific instructions on how to use Eyebright externally, using drops which "taketh away the darknesse and dimnesse of the eyes, and cleareth the sight". He also advocates taking it internally for the same purposes, as well as improving the memory. Culpeper, too, recommends it internally for "a weak brain, or memory", hence it was much in demand!

Apart from lotions for the eyes, Eyebright has developed a considerable repu tation for helping to reduce excessive catarrh. Mrs Grieve quotes Dr Fernie's experimentation with giving the herb: high overdosage seemed to increase phlegm production, but normal doses reduced both catarrh and hay fever symptoms. Known by its Latin name of *Euphrasia*, it is one of the most important homoeopathic remedies for these conditions.

### Cultivation

Eyebright is slightly parasitic in its growth, relying on roots of grass and other plants for part of its nourishment, obtained through underground suckers. Its needs are few, however, so no real damage is done to the grass.

Due to this need, Eyebright is best grown in grass. It likes dry pastures, and good drainage is essential, such as a chalky soil.

### Modern Medicinal Uses

Eyebright has astringent and anti-inflammatory properties, which have obvious benefits in local applications to watery, inflamed conditions of the eyes. A compress with soaked cotton wool pads, or an eye-bath, with a sterile solution, is very soothing. Similarly, it can be used in tincture form as a mouthwash or gargle.

Internally, it helps to reduce the excessive production of watery phlegm in problems such as hay fever or rhinitis, and tone the swollen mucous membranes. In acute attacks of hay fever, nasal congestion, sinusitis, etc., an infusion can be taken every couple of hours to give relief.

# Fennel

*Foeniculum vulgare*, Umbelliferae

### Description

Although Fennel is found growing wild in many parts of Europe, including southern Britain, it was originally indigenous to the Mediterranean lands. From there it spread northwards, and also east into Asia, as far as India. Since it has been cultivated for such a long time, various sub-species have developed with differences in height, bushiness, and so on.

From the strong, perennial roots grow strong, smooth, green stems up to four or even five feet high. These branch out a great deal, and carry extremely finely divided leaves. The large umbels of yellow flowers bloom in July and August. Later, when the fruits ripen, the umbels tend to droop. The seeds are banana-shaped, with longitudinal ridges, and vary in colour from green to light brown. Both the leaves and especially the seeds have a strong aroma, like a cross between aniseed and liquorice.

## HISTORY AND ORIGINS

Fennel was much cultivated by the Romans, for both the seeds and young edible shoots — there is a species called Florence Fennel which is grown to this day for its large bulbous base, which is braised like cooked celery or chopped into salads. Since Fennel is a digestive stimulant and very effective carminative, relieving flatulence, the Romans valued it to help them with their large meals.

Culinary uses of Fennel seeds, and the feathery leaves, spread into Europe and are mentioned in Anglo-Saxon recipes. A traditional association was with oily fish, and this seems to be a good instance of herbs being combined with foods not just for their flavour but for health reasons, since the Fennel helps to cut through the oiliness of the fish, or, as Culpeper says, "it consumes the phlegmatic humour which fish most plentifully afford and

Fennel from *Herbarium Vivae Eicones* by Otto Brunfels, 1537.

annoy the body with". The Emperor Charlemagne was very fond of Fennel in dishes, and encouraged its spread through Europe.

A number of different medicinal actions were ascribed to Fennel; for instance, it was thought to help eyesight, and Gerard gives a typical account of this virtue: "The pouder of the seed of Fennell drunke for certaine daies together fasting preserveth the eye-sight". Interestingly, Culpeper gives a more rational account of its value, saying, "The distilled water of the whole herb, or the concentrated juice dissolved … dropped into the eyes cleanses them from mists and films that hinder the sight."

Fennel was also attributed with the property of "making them lean that are apt to be fat"; William Coles, in 1650, wrote that Fennel was frequently used in drinks "for those that are grown fat, to abate their unwieldiness and cause them to grow more gaunt and lank". The ancient Greek name for the plant means to grow thin. The reason for this property partly lies in the diuretic action, and partly in Fennel's ability to reduce appetite; in times past when sermons were very long, people would chew Fennel seeds to reduce hunger pangs, so they came to be called "go-to-meeting-seeds".

Another area of use is well described by Culpeper, who says: "The leaves or seed, boiled in barley water, and drunk, are good for nurses, to increase their milk, and make it more wholesome for the child." As Fennel contains oestrogenic-like principles, this is perhaps not surprising, and it does indeed act as a galactogogue, stimulating breast-milk.

Its chief use, though, was to 'break wind', and Fennel is a prime ingredient of many traditional gripe-waters for infantile colic. It was further used with purgative medicines, as a flavouring and to relieve griping pains. Some digestive liqueurs are strongly flavoured with Fennel, for similar purposes.

## CULTIVATION

Fennel is really quite easy to grow, although the late ripening of the seeds means that it may need to be started off early in a seed-tray. It likes a sunny site, and has no particular requirements in soil

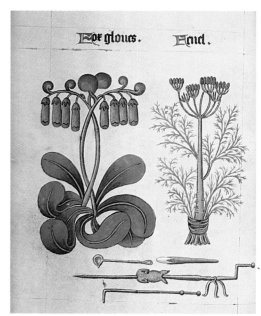

Foxglove and Fennel from *The Herbal and Bestiary*, c. 1510—20.

fertility. The plant will readily self-sow, and the problem will soon become one of hoeing out unwanted seedlings. Propagation by division of the roots in March is another method. Fennel is a hardy perennial, and will succeed in most parts of Britain.

## MODERN MEDICINAL USES

Some of Fennel's properties have already been mentioned; its effects on the digestive tract, reducing flatulence and increasing digestive tone, confirm traditional uses. For infantile colic it may be given to the mother if she is still breast-feeding, and this is doubly helpful given its actions on breast-milk production. Sterile local applications and eyewashes are valuable to reduce inflammation in, say, conjunctivitis. Its diuretic activity may be used in instances of fluid retention or bladder irritability.

# Feverfew

*Chrysanthemum parthenium*, Compositae

## DESCRIPTION

Feverfew is a fairly common weed of wasteland, found throughout Britain and

Europe, especially southern areas, but also found in many other parts of the world. It produces masses of daisy-like flowers, yellow with white outer rays; the similarity of these to Chamomile flowers has occasionally led to confusion over its botanical origins, but the leaves are nothing like as finely divided as the Chamomile's.

The upright stem is another point of difference, growing some two to three feet high, with dark-green leaves which are much divided and almost shiny in appearance. There is a variety, *Chrysanthemum parthenium aureum*, which has golden-green leaves and is often grown as a more ornamental plant, as is a double-flowered variety. The whole plant exudes a bitter smell, and the leaves taste intensely bitter.

## HISTORY AND ORIGINS

Feverfew is an interesting example of a herb where traditional areas of use have been supplanted, or perhaps supplemented by quite recent medical actions. In the last few years, Feverfew has attracted a great deal of popularity, and also much scientific research, as a remedy for migraines or headaches, yet its value in the past was for quite different conditions.

As its name suggests, Feverfew was highly valued for treating feverish illnesses, or 'agues' as they were generally called. Like all bitters it had a tonic effect on the digestion, and was considered to be a general tonic; Gerard says that dried Feverfew taken with honey "purgeth by siege melancholy and flegme", while Culpeper advises it for those that "are troubled with melancholy and heaviness, or sadness of the spirits".

The major traditional uses of Feverfew, however, were in menstrual problems, as it is a stimulant to the uterine muscles. Culpeper stresses these properties; for instance, after labour he says "it cleanses the womb, expels the afterbirth, and does a woman all the good she can desire of an herb". He further states that "it is chiefly used for the disease of the mother, whether it be the strangling or

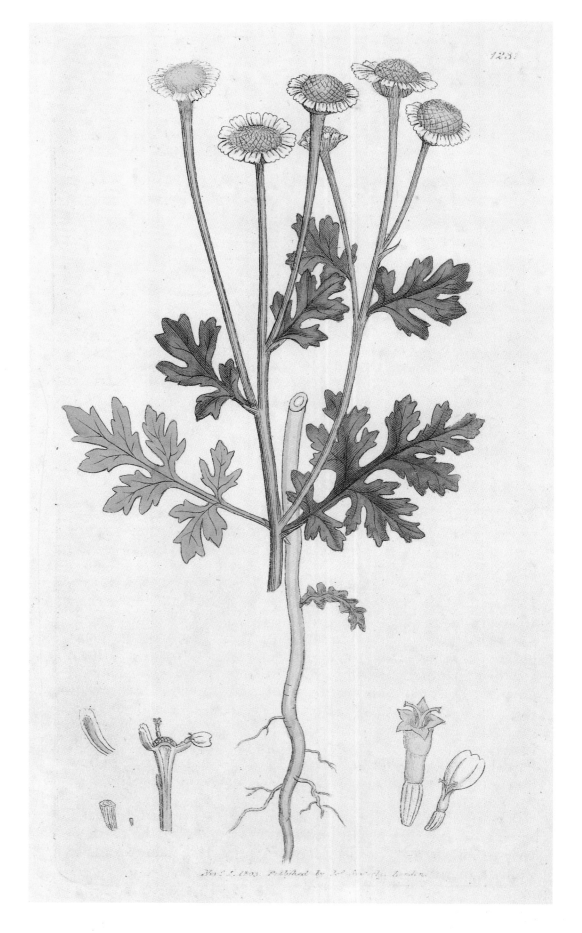

Common Feverfew *Pyrethrum parthenium* from *Sowerby's English Botany*, 1804.

L. Solis oculus.
I. Marella.
G. Maroine.

17

L. Parthenium ple.
Gr. Matercruyt ofte
Mutterkraut.

Feverfew from *Hortus Floridus* by Crispin de Pass, 1614.

rising of the mother, or hardness or inflammations of the same...." This advice makes more sense, although less fun when the term 'mother' is understood to mean the uterus!

As far as head problems are concerned, the historical uses were for sensations of vertigo and giddiness, especially if aggravated by cold. This pattern fits in very well with modern knowledge, since the vasodilatory effect of Feverfew improves head conditions, migraines, etc., which are the result of excessive constriction of the blood vessels, and which are temporarily relieved by local application of warmth to the head.

### CULTIVATION

Feverfew is a prolific spreader, often found as an invasive weed, so the pro-blem for most gardeners will be to restrict spread rather than propagation. As a herbaceous perennial, it requires very little attention to thrive for years. Two or three plants can provide ample leaves, in mild winters all the year round, for self-medication. Seeds should be sown in early spring, and planted out to permanent positions in May/June. Propagation can also be carried out by root division, again in spring, or by cuttings.

### MODERN MEDICINAL USES

As mentioned, the most popular uses of Feverfew today are for migraines. Herbal practitioners will be concerned to establish the kind of headache pattern to see if the anti-inflammatory benefits of the plant are most appropriate; these are sometimes used in treating acute phases of arthritic conditions. It should be noted that a small number of people who take Feverfew develop mouth ulcers; this only applies when taking the *fresh* leaves, and this reaction disappears on stopping the herb.

The stimulant effects on the digestion and the menstrual flow are still employed in professional practice; for obvious reasons it is best avoided in pregnancy, and women self-dosing for headaches would do well to seek advice if periods are disturbed in any way.

## Foxglove

*Digitalis purpurea*, Scrophulariaceae

### DESCRIPTION

The Foxglove is one of the most attractive of our native wild flowers, and is to be found throughout Europe as well as further afield. Normally it grows as a biennial, although it may persist for a number of years. It needs very little in the way of soil, or moisture, and will often self-seed in wasteland, by the sides of roads or on building sites, as well as in its more usual habitat of woodlands or rocky grassland.

In the first year of growth, a rosette of large, pointed and hairy leaves develops; the next year sees the growth of the long, flowering stems, sometimes over four feet high. They carry long spikes of flowers from June to August — these are well known, shaped like drooping bells and varying in colour from purplish-crimson with a white border to a pale, overall pinkish-white.

Foxgloves are a great favourite of bees and other insects, yet are not eaten by any animals, which is a good indication of their potentially poisonous nature.

### HISTORY AND ORIGINS

The name of the Foxglove is a corruption of the old term 'folksglove', and refers to the shape of the flowers, which were thought to be used as the gloves of the 'Little Folk' or fairies. Most country names revolve around this idea, or that of thimbles for the fingers, which led Fuchs to name the plant *Digitalis* in 1542.

Historical uses of the plant were varied and quite different to their modern medicinal value; often it was employed in ointments for skin disorders such as scrofula, or the 'King's Evil'. Culpeper mentions this among other uses, saying that it is "of a gentle cleansing quality, and withal very friendly to nature"! He does, however, recognize that it can be quite potent and advises it to "cleanse and purge the body both upwards and downwards".

Gerard was more dismissive, and stated of Foxgloves, "yet are they of no use, neither have they any place amongst medicines, according to the Antients". Nevertheless, Foxgloves were given in folk medicines for dropsy, or fluid retention, although the vomiting and purging due to large doses may have been considered more significant than the diuretic effects.

However, in the eighteenth century Foxgloves were thoroughly researched and prescribed by a young doctor called William Withering. It was his careful observations and recording of case-notes that established the major actions of

Purple Foxglove from Gerard's *Herball*.

*Digitalis*, safer dosages and adverse reactions, and his *Account of the Foxglove*, published in 1785, is a classic example of medical investigation of a remedy.

Despite his cautionary observations, many physicians continued to give massive doses for their emetic and purgative effects, often with fatal consequences. Interestingly, Withering strongly recommends learning about the virtues of herbal medicines from empirical knowledge and experience, which has been the traditional source for herbalists for centuries, rather than the animal-experimentation, laboratory approach just starting to be favoured by physicians at the time.

### CULTIVATION

Foxglove does best when self-seeded, but can be raised from seed sown in spring — these are very fine and are usefully mixed with sand to give more even sowing. The plant does not like chalky soils, and prefers light shade, but any well-drained site will be likely to succeed.

### MODERN MEDICINAL USES

Following Dr Withering's accounts, much work has been done on the Foxglove, and the most important glycosides have been isolated, for instance Digitoxin, and nowadays synthetic versions are often prescribed. The cumulative toxicity of these compounds means that *Digitalis* is only available on prescription from a doctor, and is not a part of herbal medicine as such. It still represents a powerful and valuable remedy in orthodox medicine, however, although regular monitoring is essential to avoid overdosage.

## Garlic

*Allium sativum*, Liliaceae

### DESCRIPTION

It is difficult to say where Garlic originated, since it has been grown in so many countries for several centuries, but probably central Asia was its original home. The appearance of the edible bulbs is extremely well known, rather like a small onion but with a pinkish-white skin and consisting of several bulblets, or cloves.

The leaves are very long and narrow, flattened like many grasses and darkish green in colour. The flowering stem rises directly from the bulb to a height of one to three feet; the flowers are white, grouped to form a typical globe shape.

### HISTORY AND ORIGINS

Garlic features in stories from the very earliest times, both as a medicine and in the diet. Indeed, it was the subject of the first recorded strike in history: when the ancient pyramids were built in Egypt, the area was quite swampy and rife with diseases, so each worker had his daily ration of Garlic to ward off ailments.

Opposite: Purple Foxglove *Digitalis purpurea* from *Hortus Medicus* by George Graves, 1834.

Pl. 1.

When a cost-cutting Pharaoh decided to dispense with this, the workers downed tools until it was reinstated!

From the Greeks and Romans through to India, Garlic was consumed in large amounts, and it is the archetypal example of the old saying, "let your food be your medicine, and your medicine be your food". Even in those days, however, there was concern about its overpowering odour. Many people felt that this conferred magical powers on Garlic, a belief which has echoed down the centuries with the idea of warding off vampires and other evils with Garlic. A strong odour of garlic is likely to keep away many people, vampires or not! On the other hand, in some rural parts of Europe, Garlic has been considered an aphrodisiac, and girls used to wear garlands of it when they went courting!

An old name for Garlic was Poor Man's Treacle, meaning a cure-all, and the ability of Garlic to increase resistance to infections was noted by the Ancients. All the old writers mention Garlic, from the Greeks through Chaucer to Culpeper, and right up to the present day. Most have described its anti-infective abilities, especially for respiratory or digestive infections, or for skin disorders.

Culpeper was more keen on this last area of use, and stated "it is a good preservative against, and a remedy for, any plague, sore, or foul ulcer; (it) takes away spots and blemishes in the skin, eases pains in the ears, ripens and breaks imposthumes, or other swellings".

Garlic gained a great reputation for its help in fighting infection during the Middle Ages and later, when towns and cities were ravaged by severe infectious diseases. The famous 'Four Thieves' Vinegar', with Garlic the principal ingredient, was a preparation used liberally, both internally and externally, by robbers who looted the bodies of plague victims, without themselves succumbing to the disease.

In more recent times, Garlic dressings for suppurating wounds and ulcers were very commonly applied in World War I, but there are countless domestic remedies involving Garlic which have been

Garlic *Allium sativum* Woodville's *Medical Botany*, 1790.

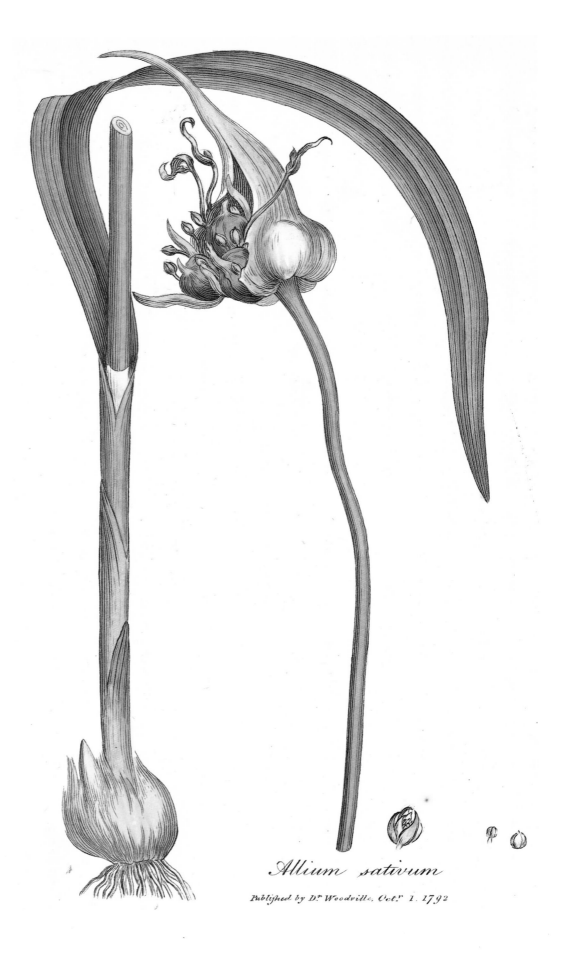

*Allium sativum*

Published by D.ʳ Woodville, Oct.ʳ 1. 1792

handed down, as well as very widespread prescriptions by herbal practitioners around the world.

## CULTIVATION

Garlic is really quite easy to grow, although for best results a sunny but moisture-retentive soil, with some well-rotted organic matter, is best. Simply divide the bulb into the corms, or cloves, and plant about two inches deep. Sowing in October and March should give enough Garlic for the year, and by retaining the largest bulbs for next year you can become self-sufficient.

## MODERN MEDICINAL USES

Much research has been carried out on Garlic, mostly abroad, and it has been established that the most active part of the plant is the smelly volatile oil. This is largely excreted from the body via the

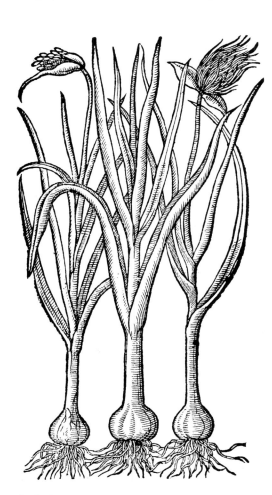

Garlic from Gerard's *Herball*.

lungs, which explain Garlic's powerful effects on respiratory infections. It helps to lower blood-pressure, temporarily at least, and over time also reduces blood cholesterol levels. For the digestive tract it encourages the development of healthy gut flora whilst resisting pathogenic, or disease-causing, organisms. Some of the conditions which it may be prescribed for are:

Frequent colds, catarrh, bronchial infections, influenza, digestive infections, externally in oil for earaches, fungal infections including *Candida* (thrush), hypertension and/or high blood cholesterol levels, thrombotic conditions, poor circulation.

# Gentian

*Gentiana lutea*, Gentianaceae

## DESCRIPTION

This Gentian is usually called the Yellow Gentian, due to the colour of its flowers, and like many other species in the genus it is a native of alpine pastures of central and southern Europe. The better-known blue-flowering species have similar properties.

Yellow Gentian has an upright stem, growing some three or four feet high, with pairs of opposite, oblong leaves at each joint. These leaves have quite prominent veins on the underside, and the leaves gradually get smaller, with shorter stalks, as they go up the stem. The yellow flowers appear in clusters in the upper leaf axils, but not until the plant is several years old — specimens have been known to live fifty years! The rhizome and roots are long and thick, with a yellow-brown colour and a very bitter taste.

## HISTORY AND ORIGINS

The generic name Gentian is said to derive from Gentius, an ancient King of Illyria (now part of Yugoslavia), who, according to the writer Dioscorides, discovered its properties. Gentius was taken

prisoner by the Romans, and the story is that they learnt of its virtues from him.

Although rarely cultivated in England, and on the Continent chiefly gathered from the wild in the mountains, it has been in great demand for centuries. Along with other bitters, Gentian has been invaluable as a tonic medicine, and in the Middle Ages it was considered almost a panacea for a wide variety of ailments. Culpeper recommends the Gentian family for stomach disorders, to neutralize poisons and toxins, to strengthen the heart and liver, and especially for agues or feverish conditions.

The key area which indicated the use of Gentian was weakness of the digestive organs, and lack of appetite, and there are numerous country liqueurs and beverages in alpine districts for use as aperitifs. From personal experience of being given such a drink in Switzerland, I can testify to its appetite-stimulating properties, as well as the alcoholic nature of the drink itself!

Before Cinchona bark, and its constituent quinine, became the remedy for use in malarial disease, Gentian was the favoured herb, and some practitioners continued to consider it superior. The bitter, stimulating properties were also valued as a remedy to expel intestinal worms, and to bring on menstruation, or "provoke the terms" as Culpeper would say.

## CULTIVATION

Yellow Gentians are the most stately of the Gentian family, and can be grown for their ornamental value, as well as for the medicinal properties of the roots. A deep, loamy soil is needed to allow the big roots to extend down a long way. The plant produces a lot of seed, and this is perhaps the best method of cultivation for any quantity of plants. Provide a reasonably sheltered and sunny site, and be prepared to wait for up to five years for flowering size to be reached.

## MODERN MEDICINAL USES

Gentian is probably the purest bitter in the herbal *materia medica*, and as such the traditional virtues of stimulating the digestive secretions, liver, and pancreas

156

*Gentiana lutea*

Published by Dr Woodville, August 1. 1792.

function are well justified. It is not irritant to the digestive tract (indeed it has some anti-inflammatory properties) and can be safely used in virtually all cases of digestive weakness, as well as being prescribed in many instances of liver or gall-bladder dysfunction.

By strengthening digestion, and diverting blood supply to the intestinal organs, Gentian has much value in febrile disorders. It appears to have a significant effect in increasing the white corpuscles in the blood, thus improving the body's defences against infections.

# Ginger

*Zingiber officinale*, Zingiberaceae

### DESCRIPTION

Ginger is thought to have been originally a native of Asia, but it is extensively grown in the West Indies and in Africa, as well as America and the Far East.

The swollen rhizome is the part used, and this is now increasingly available in shops and supermarkets, as well as the dried, ground powder. The rhizome is perennial, creeping and spreading underground. Each year it throws up reed-like stems, with very narrow, lanceolate leaves, which die down in autumn. The flowering stalks, rising directly from the rhizome, have yellow-white blooms. All parts carry a characteristic aroma, the cut fresh rhizome having an almost lemony smell, with an underlying pungency.

### HISTORY AND ORIGINS

Whether as a food or as a medicine, the major uses of Ginger seem to have been fairly consistent over many centuries. Its use spread into Europe from Greek and Roman times, but there was a considerable increase in its availability and popularity following its introduction into Spain from the East Indies by Francisco de Mendosa. The Spaniards were also

Opposite: Gentian *Gentiana lutea* Woodville's *Medical Botany*, 1790.

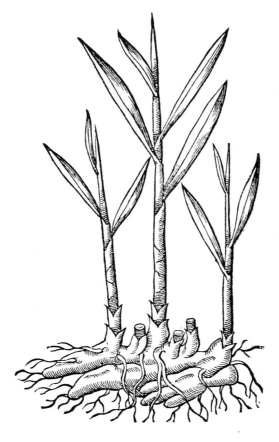

Ginger from Gerard's *Herball*.

instrumental in sending the plant to America, where large amounts were quickly cultivated from the sixteenth century onwards.

In Britain, cultivation of Ginger was at best uncertain; Gerard says, "Ginger is most impatient of the coldnesses of these our Northerne regions . . . as soone as it hath beene but touched with the first sharpe blast of Winter, it hath presently perished both blade and root." As a consequence, use of Ginger was largely confined to the dried rhizome, sliced, powdered or preserved.

Gerard well sums up the properties of Ginger: he writes: "Ginger, as Dioscorides reporteth, is right good with meat in sauces, or otherwise in conditures; for it is of an heating and digesting qualitie, and is profitable for the stomacke, and effectually opposeth it selfe against all darknesse of the sight; answering the qualities and effects of Pepper."

As might be expected, Ginger forms an important role in West Indian medicine, for flatulent indigestion and colicky pains, for any condition due to the cold, and as a rub in rheumatic problems.

### CULTIVATION

Ginger is not really suitable for growing in this country, except in greenhouses or similar conditions, and with widespread sale of fresh as well as dried rhizomes this is not necessary.

### MODERN MEDICINAL USES

Ginger is an excellent stimulant to the circulation, warming the whole system and by dilating the blood vessels encouraging blood supply to the extremities — a 'Heineken' of the herb world! As a carminative and anti-spasmodic it has great value in flatulence, especially in the bowels. The circulatory effects are supported by an expectorant action which means that Ginger is a key part of many prescriptions for colds, flu and bronchitis. On a more general level, its properties render it helpful in a number of ailments where cold or dampness aggravate the symptoms.

An area that has attracted recent research is its benefits in travel-sickness, morning-sickness and drug-induced nausea, and Ginger tea, or perhaps even Ginger biscuits, are very useful home remedies in these problems.

# Guaiacum

*Guaiacum officinale*, Zygophyllaceae

### DESCRIPTION

Guaiacum, also known as Lignum vitae, is an attractive evergreen tree that grows in the West Indies, parts of Florida and the northern coastal regions of South America.

It can grow up to some sixty feet, with a trunk circumference of five to six feet. The bark is greenish-brown, furrowed and extremely heavy; commercially, the heartwood is obtained in small pieces, and a simple test is to see if they sink in water. The oval, pinnate leaves are a glossy green and the flowers are a pretty

11

*Amomium Zingiber.*

Published by D.ʳ Woodville. March 1.1790.

blue colour. The wood has a sharp, acrid taste, but gives off a pleasant aroma when heated.

## HISTORY AND ORIGINS

From its earliest discovery by explorers Guaiacum has been valued as a timber tree, since it is very hard and durable. It was used by turners to create all manner of items, such as ships' blocks, pulleys, pestles, rulers, etc.

Around the same time, it was brought to the attention of the Spaniards in the Caribbean that Guaiacum was the traditional treatment for syphilis. Since the mainstay of conventional prescribing at that time was high levels of mercury (often with fatal results), this alternative was eagerly seized upon and brought to Europe in 1508.

During the sixteenth century, Guaiacum became very big business as a remedy for syphilis, the monopoly of its import being captured by the Fugger family, the leading bankers in Europe, in exchange for loans to the Spanish throne. The nature of the treatment was arduous, involving intense sweating and a strict dietary regimen for some time; many people found forty days or so of sweating and confinement with very little food, no wine or women, too difficult to complete! Gradually its use faded and mercury, although much more toxic and unpleasant, resumed its place as the most likely treatment.

The wood, often sold as shavings, or else the extracted resin which seemed to carry the main therapeutic properties, continued to be sold by apothecaries as a remedy for skin disorders, rheumatic complaints, gout and so forth. The recognized circulatory stimulant effects, combined with mild diuretic and laxative properties, were considered valuable in cleansing the body of impurities.

## CULTIVATION

Guaiacum is both a native of the Caribbean regions and very slow growing, so it is not appropriate to think of cultivating it in this country. The wood can be

Opposite: Ginger *Zingiber officinalis* Woodville's *Medical Botany*, 1790.

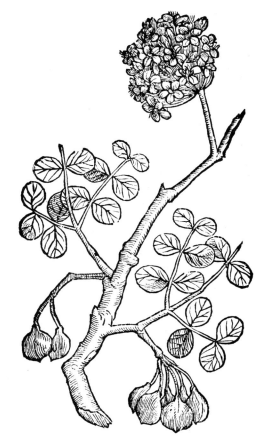

Guaiacum from Gerard's *Herball*.

obtained from herbal suppliers, but its potential for provoking an acute inflammatory reaction means that it is best left to professional prescription.

## MODERN MEDICINAL USES

The major action of Guaiacum is as a strong stimulant to the peripheral circulation; if the patient is kept warm, then it can increase sweating considerably. The area of modern use is in chronic rheumatic disorders, both to reduce the need for local inflammation and to encourage elimination.

# Hawthorn

*Crataegus oxyacanthoides*, Rosaceae

## DESCRIPTION

Hawthorn trees are found throughout the northern hemisphere, in temperate zones. The tree is shrubby in appearance, but can reach some thirty feet. It is very thorny and much-branching, and has been extensively used in hedging — the word 'haw' relates to the German *hage*, or hedge.

The small leaves have three lobes, and the white or pink flowers cover the tree with blossom in late spring/early summer, hence the country name of May. In autumn the distinctive red 'haws', or fruits, resemble miniature apples; the white flesh of the fruits encases a single stone. The blossoms give off an almost overpowering odour.

## HISTORY AND ORIGINS

In olden times, the Hawthorn was considered sacred, being thought to be the source of the crown of thorns given to Jesus, and before that it was believed to keep away sickness. The Latin names derive from the words for sharp thorn, and also hardness of the wood; the close grain of the wood and its ability to be highly polished meant that it was in demand for small articles such as boxes, combs, etc. It will burn at a great heat, and charcoal from it was used to melt pig-iron in the early days of the Industrial Revolution.

From archaeological evidence, it seems that our ancestors often ate large quantities of Hawthorn berries, and the leaves are still remembered by some people by their country name of 'bread-and-cheese', since they were put into sandwiches by farm workers.

The medicinal value of Hawthorn has been greatly appreciated throughout Europe for centuries, different countries placing emphasis on the benefit of using the leaves, flowers or fruits. A traditional reason for prescribing Hawthorn was for urinary stones; Louise Bourgeois, the midwife of Maria de' Medici, is known to have given it to many patients for kidney stones, and Culpeper says: "The seeds in the berries beaten to powder being drunk in wine, are good against the stone and dropsy."

It is in this latter area of heart-related problems that Hawthorn has the greatest reputation, especially over the last two hundred years. As a cardiac relaxant it has been highly valued by many physicians, Dr Fiessinger coining the phrase

*Guaiacum officinale.*

Published by D.ʳ Woodville April. 1. 1790.

Hawthorn from Gerard's *Herball*.

"valerian of the heart", and long clinical observations of its benefits, and its lack of toxicity have confirmed its high standing. On a lighter note, Palaiseul quotes an old folk invocation to Hawthorn, to "stop my husband from beating me and change him into a donkey that I may make him carry the straw"!

## CULTIVATION

Hawthorn is probably sufficiently wide-spread not to need to grow in the garden, but a hedge can be created over time, or else a single tree can be planted. Whilst this can be done from seed, buying a sapling will save years of patience.

Opposite: Guaiacum or Lignum Vitae Tree *Guaiacum officinale* from Woodville's *Medical Botany*, 1790.

Wedge-leaved Hawthorn *Crataegus oxyacanthoides* from *Edwards's Botanical Register*, 1827.

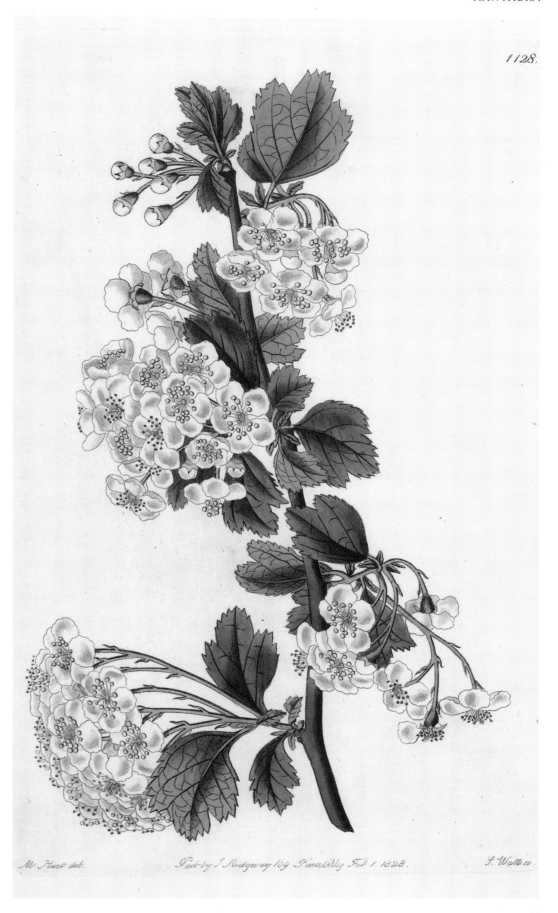

## Modern Medicinal Uses

Hawthorn is probably the most valuable cardiac tonic remedy for the medical herbalist. It acts to dilate the coronary arteries, as well as being a dilator of the peripheral blood vessels, and also stabilizes contractions of the heart muscles. It has a mild diuretic effect as well, and is prescribed for a whole range of cardiac and circulatory conditions, such as angina, poor circulation and symptoms of atherosclerosis, anxiety-induced palpitations, etc.

The effects of Hawthorn, for instance on regulating blood-pressure, are normally only seen over time, and long-term prescription is the usual pattern. Its lack of toxicity makes it very suitable for this type of situation, provided professional diagnosis and treatment are sought.

# Heartsease

*Viola tricolor*, Violaceae

## Description

Heartsease, or the Wild Pansy, is a beautiful, annual wild flower growing on hilly pastures throughout Britain, Europe, America and into Asia. Wild meadows of the kind still found in alpine pastures, but all too rarely in this country, are a typical habitat.

The colouring pattern of the flowers has a great variation, the three colours of its Latin title, purple, yellow and white, showing up in varying amounts and shades. It blooms through the summer, growing to about eighteen inches at times, either upright or more prostrate in form. It is distinguished from other Violas by the more indented shape of its foliage, and by its freely branching habit.

## History and Origins

Heartsease has possibly more country names than any other plant, and this shows how long and widespread its popularity has been. Shakespeare makes much of its reputation in love charms, especially in *A Midsummer Night's Dream*,

and it was a favourite in English gardens from earliest times.

The common name of pansy derives from the French *pensée*, and an interesting reference to this is given by Mrs Grieve. The physician to Louis XV and founder of the 'Economists', Quesnay, was given the nickname 'The Thinker', and his coat of arms bore three pansy flowers.

Traditional medical uses were varied; the flowers were made into cordials for heart complaints, and the whole herb was employed for inflamed skin disorders, chest complaints, and feverish illnesses in children which often led to infantile convulsions. Both Gerard and

Heartsease *Viola tricolor* from Woodville's *Medical Botany*, 1790.

Culpeper state similar indications, the latter saying: "The spirit of it is excellent good for convulsions in children, and a remedy for falling sickness, inflammation of the lungs and breasts, pleurisy, scabs, itch, &c."

In former times it was listed in the *US Pharmacopoeia* for eczema and other skin complaints, both externally and internally. For these and chronic bronchial infections it has been the most consistently used. A syrup was the favourite preparation, although tinctures and also ointments are frequently mentioned.

## CULTIVATION

Heartsease can quite easily and successfully be grown from seed, and one of the best aspects of the recent revival of interest in wild flowers is the number of such seeds that are available to gardeners — nearly all the show gardens at Chelsea in 1990 seemed to contain Heartsease!

It has quite modest needs from the soil, often found on waste ground, but a sunny site shows it off to best advantage. It will self-seed, but fresh sowings each year may be needed for greatest effect.

## MODERN MEDICINAL USES

Amongst other constituents, Heartsease contains salicylates, and these contribute towards its anti-inflammatory properties. It additionally exerts laxative, diuretic and expectorant effects, and is best used in complex disorders such as eczema, rheumatoid arthritis and other examples of what are termed auto-immune disease, where it can be very helpful indeed. Particular indications for Heartsease are eczema where there is weeping exudate from the skin, whooping cough and bronchitis, and cystitis with painful urination.

Heartsease from Mrs Loudon's *The Ladies' Flower-Garden of Ornamental Annuals*, 1840. 1. *Viola tricolor* 2. *V. lutea* 4, 5, 6 and 7. Hybrids and varieties of Heartsease.

DE

WONDEREN

GODS

in de

minſt geachtste

SCHEPSELEN.

II. Deel.

# Hops

*Humulus lupulus*, Cannabinaceae

## DESCRIPTION

Hops are the only representative of its genus to be native to Britain, and it is found from Europe through to Asia, growing wild in hedgerows and woodland edges. It is a perennial climber, with a thick root and a twining, flexible stem that can extend for twenty feet or more. The rough, heart-shaped leaves have finely toothed edges, and normally occur in pairs.

The flowers are either male, hanging in loose bunches, or female, in tightly packed, conical catkins. These are the strobiles that are used in medicine and brewing; they are initially greenish, but on fertilizing they change to yellow-brown. They have a strong and distinctive odour, and a bitter taste.

## HISTORY AND ORIGINS

Hops seem to get their first mention by Pliny, who describes the Roman habit of eating the young shoots in spring as a bitter cleanser and appetizer. They are still occasionally eaten as a vegetable, especially on the Continent, and are considered quite a local delicacy in parts of Italy. Culpeper says that the young Hop shoots "boiled and served up like asparagus, are a very wholesome as well as a pleasant tasted spring food".

From the Middle Ages Hops have been used in brewing, starting probably in Holland in the fourteenth century. In Britain they were not used for another couple of hundred years; in this country traditionally a variety of bitter herbs have been used in the making of ale, such as mugwort or ground ivy. The term 'beer', from the Germanic *bier*, referred to liquors made with the recent introduction, Hops. Indeed, there was considerable opposition at first to the use of Hops in alcohol, calling it "a wicked

Opposite: Decorative title-page by Sepp from his *Beschouwing der Wonderen Gods*, 1786. On the left-hand side the Queen of Spain Fritillary is shown above its food plant, the viola.

Hops from Gerard's *Herball*.

weed that would spoil the taste of the drink and endanger the people".

As for the medicinal indications for Hops, Culpeper has this to say: "This will open obstructions of the liver and spleen, cleanse the blood, loosen the belly, cleanse the reins from gravel, and provoke urine." Most of these actions are allied to the bitter nature of the plant, and many writers testify to its effects as a digestive stimulant.

On quite a different note, it was also recognized quite early on that the volatile oil had sedative effects, and Hops were given as a draught to induce sleep. Hop pillows have been used at times, George III being a particular devotee (although he was later pronounced insane!), despite the unpleasantly strong smell. Hops, and in particular their chief active constituent Lupulin, were official in both Britain and the USA at times.

## CULTIVATION

Parts of south-east England, as well as elsewhere in Europe and beyond, have become dedicated to the growing of Hops for brewing. They require a deep, rich soil with good drainage, and propagation is usually by cuttings or suckers from old shoots. A fair amount of organic matter is needed for good growth; plants do not get to full capacity until the second or third year. They are also prone to various diseases, from aphis to mildew.

## MODERN MEDICINAL USES

Hops are a good bitter digestive tonic, with a strong anti-spasmodic effect on the intestinal tract being helpful in many anxiety-related digestive disturbances like colic or spastic constipation. As a sedative to the central nervous system they are valuable in nervousness and insomnia, but they can induce mental depression in over-dosage. Beer drinkers demonstrate these actions well; initial relaxation of inhibiting centres in the brain, with various results, inexorably leads on to a state of melancholy.

# Horsetail

*Equisetum arvense*, Equisetaceae

## DESCRIPTION

Horsetails are found in all temperate regions; they are a very old and primitive form of plant, unlike any others in Britain. Millions of years ago, in the Carboniferous period, they and their ancient relatives probably covered the Earth, and they form a good proportion of our coal deposits.

From the creeping rhizome each spring rise up fertile, spore-carrying stems, rather like asparagus in appearance. As these wither, the infertile stems appear. These consist of upright, hollow and much-jointed stems of pale green. Each stem is grooved and the joints end in sharp sheaths instead of proper leaves. The shape gives rise in folk-names, to many such as bottle brush, shave-grass and so on.

Pl. 41

*Humulus Lupulus.*

W. Clark del. et sculp.

London, Published by John Churchill, Leicester Square, Nov.ʳ 1827.

## History and Origins

The sterile stems of Horsetail contain a great deal of silica, and for centuries they were used for polishing and scouring metal, pewter and wooden vessels. Cabinet-makers also employed them in polishing.

Very young shoots seem to have been occasionally eaten by the Romans as a vegetable, prepared like asparagus, but they are not very appetizing, and animals generally avoid them, although in various countries farmers have experimented with giving them as fodder.

The medicinal uses, which are confined to the sterile stems, have been mostly as a diuretic and to stop bleeding, due to its highly astringent nature. Culpeper advised: "It is very powerful to stop bleeding either inward or outward ... The decoction, taken in wine, provokes urine, and helps the stone and strangury." In the nineteenth century, the Abbé Kneipp, the German priest who virtually re-invented hydrotherapy and strongly advocated natural remedies, recommended Horsetail particularly in urinary disorders.

Another medicinal indication was as a natural source of minerals, notably the silica but including many others, and especially on the Continent it was prescribed for tubercular patients, and generally in convalescence.

## Cultivation

Horsetails develop, as described, from spores, in a similar fashion to ferns. They can also be propagated by means of the tuberous rhizomes. They naturally grow in moist places, but can flourish in a garden near water, or in a shady spot. A clay, moisture-retentive soil is perhaps best, although a sandy soil can be quite adequate, with no particular requirements for nutrients, the plants often thriving in waste ground.

## Modern Medicinal Uses

Horsetail has a strongly astringent effect, especially on the membranes lining the urinary tract, and is furthermore quite a

Hops *Humulus lupulus* from *English Botany*, Syme 1868.

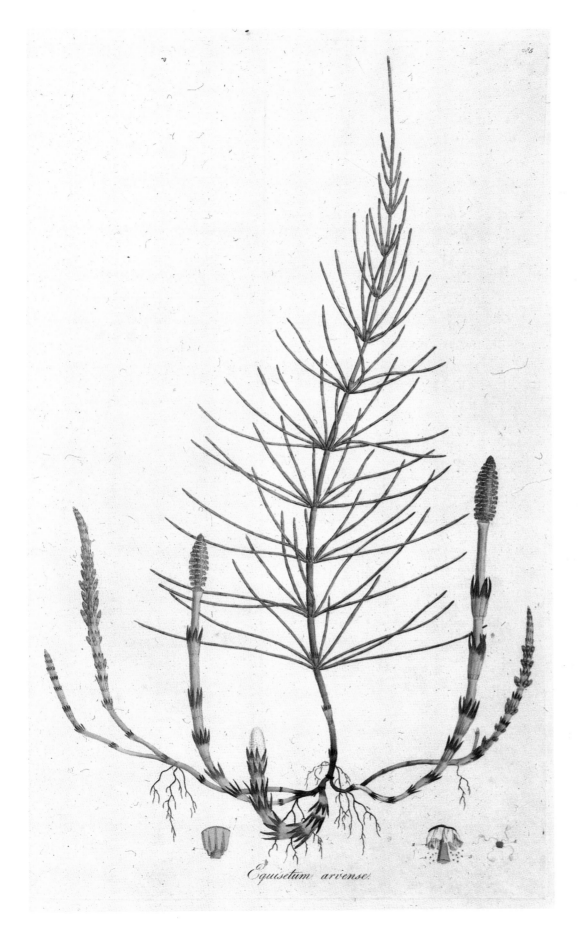

*Equisetum arvense.*

powerful diuretic, so that disorders of the urinary system are its major area of benefit. Irritability of the urinary tract, for example in bed-wetting, fluid retention, chronic cystitis or inflamed prostate gland, are the kind of problems where Horsetail might be prescribed.

Its ability to stem bleeding is well founded, but blood in the urine can be a symptom of serious illness and should always be properly diagnosed and treated. The high mineral content of Horsetail can be valuable to help tissue regeneration after illness, for instance bronchial infections.

# Hyssop

*Hyssopus officinalis*, Labiatae

### DESCRIPTION

Hyssop is an attractive, bushy, perennial herb that originated in the Mediterranean area, but is now widely grown in Britain and elsewhere. It can reach up to four feet in height, although two feet is more normal in colder climates.

It has square stems, and small, narrow leaves, with one-sided spikes of blue flowers in whorls. It is possible to get pink- or white-flowered varieties. The plant is pleasantly fragrant.

### HISTORY AND ORIGINS

Hyssop has very ancient origins, the name itself deriving from the Greek word for 'holy herb', since it was used in cleansing temples; it is mentioned in the Bible: "Purge me with Hyssop, and I shall be clean" (although there is some doubt over exactly which plant was meant). Hippocrates prescribed it for bronchial problems, and Dioscorides thought it was so familiar to his readers in the first century AD that he did not bother to describe it.

Probably the chief medicinal use of Hyssop was in respiratory complaints; Gerard advises that, "A decoction of Hyssope made with figges, water, honey, and rue, and drunken, helpeth

Horsetail *Equisetum arvense* from *Flora Londinensis* by W. Curtis, 1746–99.

the old cough." Culpeper is a little more forthcoming, and suggests that Hyssop, boiled with honey, "helps those that are troubled with coughs, shortnesse of breath, wheezing and rheumatic distillations upon the lungs". He also lists other indications, such as quinsy, dropsy and external use for bruises and wounds, but his highest regard is for Hyssop's ability to expectorate tough phlegm in chest diseases.

In the Middle Ages Hyssop was greatly used in cooking, the chopped leaves giving a pungent aroma to savoury dishes, The intense, almost camphor-like aroma of the volatile oil has been long appreciated by the perfumery industry, and it was often grown near bee-hives to try to impart its flavour to the honey.

Many liqueurs have included Hyssop, most famously Green Chartreuse. These herbal, concentrated alcoholic drinks were partly devised as a way of preserving the properties of herbs, to provide a tonic for the monks and others, but can be enjoyed, in small quantities, for their flavours alone.

An interesting old recommendation was as a vermifuge, to kill intestinal worms, an indication which has no modern following; this might be a useful subject for research, since the oil has some parasiticidal effects. However, there is a cautionary note to be sounded on the toxicity of the essential oil at high levels.

### CULTIVATION

Hyssop likes a dry, light soil in a sunny position, but will tolerate other situations. It is quite a hardy perennial; plants can be raised either from seed or from cuttings, taken in spring or autumn. It can make a good, bushy edging plant for a herb garden; some occasional cutting in of the plants is all that is required to keep them within bounds.

### MODERN MEDICINAL USES

Hyssop is an excellent relaxing expectorant, valuable in loosening coughs with thick, sticky phlegm. It encourages sweating in the feverish person, and is often prescribed in colds or 'flu, when its relaxing properties can also be helpful in

*Hyssopus officinalis.*

Published by D.ʳ Woodville. Jan.ʸ 1. 1791.

Hyssop *Hyssopus officinalis* from Woodville's *Medical Botany*, 1790.

allowing the patient to get adequate rest. This can be particularly useful for children.

As a carminative, it is of use in digestive upsets and flatulence, and it helps poor circulation by dilating the peripheral blood vessels. Its main indications are nevertheless for respiratory complaints, confirming traditional experience. The calming effects are equally useful in more generalized anxiety states, but combine well with the expectorant properties in bronchial ailments.

Opposite: Hyssop *Hyssopus officinalis* from *Getreue Darstellung…Arzneykund…*, F.G. Haynes 1819.

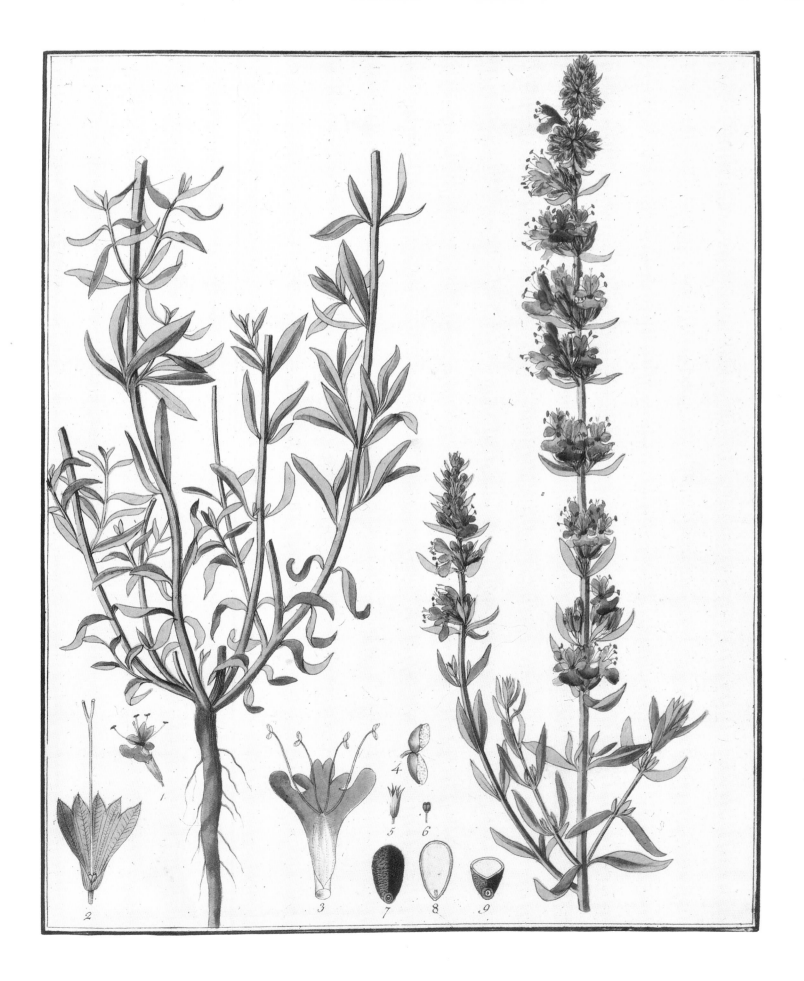

2

3

4

5

6

7

8

9

# Iris

*Iris germanica* 'Florentina', Iridaceae

## DESCRIPTION

The Iris family has been famous for centuries for its stately shape and beautiful flowers. The Iris most famed for producing Orris root is *Iris germanica* 'Florentina', formerly called *Iris florentina*, and like other Irises it has tall, swordlike leaves, in this case of a blue-green colour. It is one of the tallest species, the flowering stems reaching some three feet in height.

This variety is much grown around Florence, at San Polo, and is a native of southern Europe. The flowers are blue-veined, sometimes verging on white tinged with lavender. As with other Irises, the flowers have three upturned petals, or standards, and three down-turned petals called falls. The style is flattened into a 'beard'. The creeping rhizomes are thick and fleshy, and are reddish-brown in colour.

Other species of relevance are *Iris pallida* and *Iris germanica*, both with blue flowers, which are more robust and therefore often used a source of Orris, and also *Iris florentina* var. *albicans*, now called simply *Iris albicans*. This latter is not of medicinal value, but produces wonderful, pure-white flowers.

## HISTORY AND ORIGINS

The Iris was considered by the Ancients to be a symbol of power and authority. From it originated the sceptre, the Egyptians placing an Iris on the brow of the Sphinx. The temple of Thutmoses III at Karnak, which is some three thousand years old, carries images of the Iris on its walls. The three-fold petals represented faith, wisdom and valour. The Iris family is named after Iris, the Greek messenger goddess whose sign was the rainbow.

In more modern times, the Fleur-de-lys has appeared on many royal coats of arms, for instance the old French royal family, the Medici dynasty and the old coat of arms of Florence, which bore a white Iris on a red background. It is also the badge of the Scout movement, so has remained a potent symbol for thousands of years.

The dried roots, powdered into Orris, were used for perfumery and medicine by the Greeks and Romans, and Orris is described by all the classical writers. The best plants were considered to come from Illyria (Dalmatia, Yugolavia), but by the Middle Ages northern Italy had become famous for its Orris production. The fresh roots smell of little except the earth, but on thorough drying they develop a characteristic, pleasant aroma rather like violets. The different species described above were all used for Orris production, and indeed were cultivated in England before the time of Gerard, but it is the Florentine variety that was considered the finest.

The fresh roots were formerly used to some extent in medicine. They have a purgative, diuretic and emetic effect in large doses; with the different species carrying similar names, there is some confusion in the old herbals as to which Iris is meant to be taken. Culpeper refers to the Blue Fleur-de-lys, probably *Iris germanica*, and gives many recommendations for its use, such as clearing phlegm and coughs, dropsy, intestinal worms and lack of menstruation to name only a few. Several of the old herbalists suggested using the dried powder as a snuff, to relieve nasal congestion. Generally, however, it was the dried Orris that was in demand, for perfumery, scenting linen and so on.

## CULTIVATION

Irises do best in rich, well-drained soil, and most importantly in a good, sunny position. The rhizomes should be just on the surface; dividing the plants can be done in spring, but harvesting is done in autumn. Irises take two or three years to grow to a sufficient size, and when dried the roots take up to two years to fully develop the aroma, so much patience is needed to make Orris at home. The plants can be grown just for their beauty, with many attractive if less perfumed varieties, such as the variegated forms.

## MODERN MEDICINAL USES

Traditional use of the fresh roots was always a hazardous exercise, due to the cathartic and emetic potential, and these Irises are not used in medicine at all now. The Blue Flag, *Iris versicolor*, which grows in eastern America and Britain, is used in moderate doses to stimulate the bowels and liver in some skin disorders, but again drying the root is necessary to reduce the irritant effects.

# Juniper

*Juniperus communis*, Coniferae

## DESCRIPTION

Junipers are found throughout Europe, North America and northern Asia, mostly on chalk downs or moorland. They can vary in size from a small bush, or even prostrate varieties, to a tree up to thirty feet high; the Juniper of medicine is, in this country, typically a shrub of around four feet, although it can reach ten feet or more.

The leaves are very narrow, almost like needles, arranged in small whorls. The tiny flowers usually appear on different plants as male or female; the male cones are some three times the size of the female ones. The fruits are initially green, taking two or three years to turn purplish-black, so that ripe and unripe fruits are found on the same bush.

## HISTORY AND ORIGINS

The wood of Juniper, in countries where it grows to tree height, has been highly valued for its ability to last a long time without rotting. Hannibal, for example, ordered Juniper wood for temples to Diana. In later centuries, alchemists made use of it for heating their retorts during long chemical experiments.

The cleansing and antiseptic properties of Juniper, especially the berries, was quickly recognized. Branches of Juniper

Opposite: Florentine Iris *Iris florentina* from Woodville's *Medical Botany*, 1790.

*Iris florentina*

Published by D.ʳ Woodville August 1. 1790.

were burnt in houses and public places to fumigate against infections and plague; Hippocrates used them in this way to protect Athens against such outbreaks. This custom was continued in quite modern times, French hospitals being fumigated with burning Juniper even into this century.

Apart from resisting infection, Juniper berries were taken for their digestive and diuretic qualities. Culpeper sums up their traditional uses very well: "(they are) counter-poison, and a resister of the pestilence, and excellent against the bites of venomous beasts; it provokes urine, and is available in dysenteries and strangury. It is a remedy against dropsy, and brings down the terms, helps the fits of the mother, expels the wind, and strengthens the stomach. Indeed there is no better remedy for wind in any part of the body, or the colic."

Aside from these straight medicinal applications, Juniper was used in cooking, especially with red meats and fish, partly for the flavour combination and partly to make the food safe to eat! This

*Juniperus Lycia*

Published by D.° Woodville June 1. 1792.

Juniper *Juniperus lycia* from Woodville's *Medical Botany*, 1790.

kind of food combining, using herbs to stop food-poisoning as well as to improve the taste, was fairly common in times past when there was no refrigeration and little hygiene.

Juniper is perhaps most famous as a flavouring for alcoholic spirits, most obviously in Geneva or Holland Gin, and gin is still very much reliant on Juniper for its taste (and diuretic effect!). In the nineteenth century, the Abbé Kneipp used to recommend eating a course of Juniper berries for internal cleansing, and suggested rubbing the tincture or oil into the limbs and joints for sciatica, rheumatic pains, lumbago and so on.

## CULTIVATION

Juniper prefers chalky soil, but by no means is this essential. What is essential

Juniper from Gerard's *Herball*.

for medicinal or culinary use is that it is the species *Juniperus communis* that is grown. Since male and female flowers are normally on separate bushes, and only female flowers produce berries, care should be taken when buying a plant. The berries can be harvested when they are black, in the autumn, and dried until a little shrivelled.

## MODERN MEDICINAL USES

There are a number of active compounds in Juniper, notably the volatile oil. It is a carminative, reducing flatulence as Culpeper accurately observed, and also acts as a digestive tonic. Equally important is its effects on increasing urine flow, whilst additionally acting as a urinary antiseptic. It helps to excrete acid waste matter, and has much value in gout and similar conditions.

**CAUTION**: Juniper has something of an irritant effect on the kidneys, hence the diuretic action, and should not be used when the kidneys are infected or inflamed. It also stimulates uterine contractions and should never be given in pregnancy. It has many valuable actions, but the advice of a medical herbalist should be sought for safety and best use.

# *Lavender*

*Lavandula officinalis*, Labiatae

## DESCRIPTION

Lavender is a shrub-like perennial that originated in the Mediterranean region, but has been cultivated for centuries in many parts of Europe, especially in France and England, and now in lands all round the world. Traditionally, the best Lavender was grown in England, mainly due to the long summer hours allowing the volatile oils time to accumulate.

There are several varieties of Lavender, but *Lavandula officinalis* and/or *Lavandula vera* is the normal name for the species used in medicine: The stems are woody in appearance, with a rather flaky bark,

and become many-branched in growth. The leaves are narrow, linear and appear in opposite pairs. The flowers rise on long, thin stems and consist of whorls of purplish-blue colour. They have a characteristic, pleasant aroma.

Other notable species are *Lavandula spicata*, or Spike Lavender, which is a coarser, broader-leaved variety found especially in mountainous areas of France and Spain, and *Lavandula stoechas*, or French Lavender, which has small, dark-violet flowers tightly packed, resembling a bottle brush.

## HISTORY AND ORIGINS

An ancient Greek name for Lavender was *Nardus*, referring to an area of cultivation, and it is frequently mentioned in old texts as Spikenard. The Romans valued it highly, and used it in garlands, to freshen linen, and most of all in bathing — the word Lavender is derived from the verb *lavare*, to wash.

Although the Romans probably introduced Lavender into Britain, it was not really cultivated here until the beginning of the sixteenth century; Gerard, for instance, grew it in his garden. Nevertheless, people were very familiar with it in dried form and in sachets, to air and perfume all the rooms of the house, clothing, etc. When the Pilgrim Fathers went to America, Lavender was one of the herbs they took along with them.

Apart from incorporating the aroma of Lavender into a myriad of household products, and using it extensively in perfumery to this day, the medicinal qualities of the plant were soon recognized. Gerard recommends it for "the panting and passion of the heart, (it) prevaileth against giddinese, turning, or swimming of the braine", and Culpeper too advises it for fainting, as well as headaches, cramps and stomach complaints, to mention just a few of his suggestions.

The use of the oil of Lavender in particular, for nervous palpitations, giddiness and fainting, became a part of official medicine, and a preparation called 'palsy drops', relying mainly on Lavender, was recognized in the *British Pharmacopoeia* for over two hundred years.

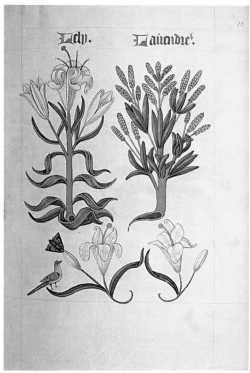

Lavender from *The Herbal and Bestiary*, c. 1510—20.

A constant feature of folk medicine has been the use of Lavender as an antiseptic, for local use on wounds, bites, burns, parasites and so on. These properties were described by the Abbess St Hildegarde of Bingen, and noted by many others since; for example, in Salmon's *Herbal* of 1710 we read: "It is good also against the bitings of serpents, mad-dogs and other venomous creature".

## CULTIVATION

Plants of Lavender can be found in every garden centre, and although it can be grown from seed, propagation is perhaps most usefully done by taking cuttings, with a 'heel' attached, in early autumn or maybe in spring.

Lavender grows best on a light soil in a sunny, dry position, but it will grow in most gardens, with decent drainage. It does not need a rich soil, indeed the oil content will be higher if there is only moderate nourishment. It can form a useful hedging for a herb border, and with varying shades of flowers, including rarer pink or white varieties, an attractive grouping can be made.

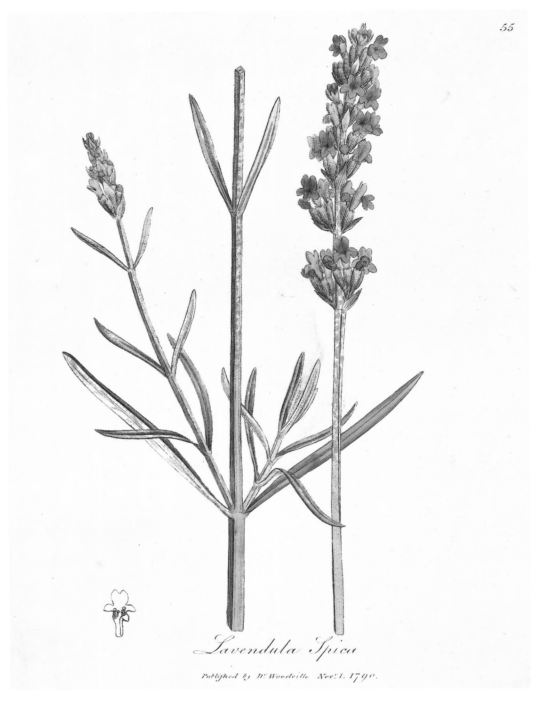

55

*Lavendula Spica*

Publifhed by Dr. Woodville Novr. 1. 1790.

Lavender *Lavandula spica* from Woodville's *Medical Botany*, 1790.

## Modern Medicinal Uses

The anti-infective, anti-spasmodic and tissue-healing properties of Lavender have been the subject of much research in recent times, and they lend themselves to all manner of local applications. Burns, muscular aches and strains, rheumatic disorders, and bruises are some of the conditions where external use of Lavender oil may be indicated.

Internally, Lavender has carminative and digestive effects that combine well with its relaxing benefits in stress-related indigestion, colic, nervous exhaustion or irritability. Many bronchial problems, especially when there is a degree of anxiety, are helped by Lavender. Overall, its wide range of properties and versatility make it a very useful domestic remedy for minor ailments, as well as important in professional practice.

Lavender from Gerard's *Herball*.

## Lime Blossom

*Tilia europaea*, Tiliaceae

### Description

The common Lime is a stately tree that is found throughout the temperate zones of the Northern Hemisphere, notably in Britain. It is really a cross between the narrow-leaved and the broad-leaved Limes, but there is nothing to distinguish between them in any uses. Apart from appearing in deciduous woodlands, it is frequently grown in parks, country estates, and as avenues in towns.

Limes can grow to a height of 120 feet. The leaves are ovate, almost heart-shaped, darkish green on the upper

Opposite: Lime Blossom from *De Stirpium* by Bock.

*Tilia europæa.*

Tab. 190.

surface and pale underneath. The pale yellow flowers hang in cymes, or flat clusters, on long stalks branching out of long, very pale green leaf bracts. When in blossom, the tree gives off a sweet, far-reaching perfume, and cars parked under Lime trees get covered with a sticky exudate.

### HISTORY AND ORIGINS

The importance of Lime blossom (the flowers and bracts are used medicinally) as a medicine through many centuries can be seen in the number of avenues that have been planted by royal decree; in France, the harvest of such avenues was often reserved for hospitals. Unter den Linden, in old Berlin, was a favourite walk of many Germans, who also drank lime tea in the cafés.

The calming effects of the aroma, and preparations from the flowers, were believed to be effective against all kinds of nervous disorders. Culpeper sums up these virtues: "The flowers are the only parts used, and are a good cephalic and nervine, excellent for apoplexy, epilepsy, vertigo, and palpitation of the heart." In fact, in ancient times, the bark was also used to make vinegars and lotions for external use on skin blemishes or eye complaints, but the flowers are the real focus of medicinal uses.

The nectar from the flowers is very attractive to bees, and Lime blossom honey is considered by many to be the finest-flavoured of all. As a flavouring in liqueurs it became popular at an early stage.

The wood is very light, close-grained and resistant to woodworm, and has been used by the finest carvers since mediaeval times. The work of Grinling Gibbons, in St Paul's Cathedral, for example, is one of the supreme examples. On a less skilled level, it has been utilized in many turned articles, and for making artists' charcoal.

Lime blossom tea is a popular drink on the Continent to aid relaxation and help sleep; this is especially true in France, where 'tilleul' can be found in most households. Messegue wrote that Lime

Opposite: Lime Blossom *Tilia europea* from *Flora Londinensis*, William Jackson Hooker 1828.

blossom was a key ingredient in his "tea of happiness", that would "bring you peaceful nights, joyful awakenings and happy days, if you will take it regularly".

### CULTIVATION

As with all trees, starting a Lime off from seed is a labour for posterity, and it is necessary to seek a sapling from a specialist nursery. I have seen one for sale at an exhibition that was over thirty feet tall, but this is both very unusual and very expensive! Their graceful shape and sweet perfume make them well worth considering in long-term plans for a garden.

### MODERN MEDICINAL USES

The relaxant properties of Lime blossom are matched by its effects on reducing spasm, especially in the blood vessels and so improving the circulation to the extremities. It additionally has diaphoretic and diuretic actions, which make it very useful in influenza or feverish colds, with restlessness and anxiety.

In modern professional practice, one of its chief areas of application is to hypertension and/or atherosclerosis, particularly when tension is one of the causes of the problems: poor circulation or varicose veins are other vascular conditions where Lime blossom may be prescribed. As a simple tea, it is very good to help anxiousness, in adults or children. Stress-related headaches, of the kind where the blood vessels constrict in spasm, can be relieved in this way.

# Marshmallow

*Althaea officinalis*, Malvaceae

### DESCRIPTION

As its name suggests, Marshmallow originated in salty marshes, damp meadows and ditches, from Europe through into northern Asia; it has been spread into America and Australia. It is a member of the Hollyhock family, and its similarity to other mallows is apparent.

Marsh Mallow from Gerard's *Herball*.

The upright stems reach some three or four feet, and carry broad, pale-green leaves. They have between three and five lobes, toothed at the edges, and have an almost velvety feel due to the covering of fine hairs. The flowers are a very pale pink, with five petals and the red stamens protruding in a tube shape. The roots are thick and long, greyish on the outside and white with long furrows inside.

### HISTORY AND ORIGINS

The Mallows in general seem to have no toxic effects, and many of them have been used as foods in the past. Marshmallow contains a great deal of mucilage, and was considered a delicacy by the Romans. Many countries, especially in the Middle East, have a similar tradition of eating the roots as a vegetable.

In France, druggists used to make a sweet paste, Pâté de Guimauve, which was given for coughs and sore throats. However, the sweets called marsh-

*Althæa officinalis*

Publifhed by Dr. Woodville Novr. 1. 1790.

mallows have no connection with the plant, being made from gum arabic, sugar and beaten egg-whites.

Marshmallow was probably introduced into Britain by the Romans, and it has enjoyed a high reputation in herbal medicine since. All the classical writers know of its benefits in soothing inflammation, both internally and as a poultice. Pliny wrote: "Whosoever shall take a spoonful of the Mallows shall that day be free from all diseases that may come to him."

The demulcent and emollient properties of Marshmallow, softening and easing painful swelling or inflamed areas, has been used in all kinds of ailments. Culpeper gives a couple of pages of recommendations, using mostly the roots or the leaves. For instance, externally he suggests its use "against all hard tumours and inflammations, imposthumes, or swellings of the testicles, or other parts", as well as bruises, burns, sprains, stings, etc. Internally he advises it for coughs, chest infections, digestive pains, urinary stones and inflammation among other problems.

Bronchial coughs and soreness seem to have been one of the major applications in mediaeval times, with people like the Abbess Hildegarde and Albertus Magnus mentioning the use of *bismalva* and *mismalva* (greater and lesser mallow).

## Cultivation

Marshmallow can be grown from seed, sown in spring, but cuttings will give a good result, and the roots could then be harvested the same year. The stems die down each autumn, and this would be the time to divide the roots for further plants. Plant about two feet apart to give plenty of room. Ideally it needs a rich, moist soil although it will grow on wasteland near a stream or ditch.

## Modern Medicinal Uses

The high concentration of mucilage, around 35% in the root, perhaps 10% in the leaf, gives the plant its characteristic

Opposite: Marsh Mallow *Althaea officinalis* from Woodville's *Medical Botany*, 1790.

taste and demulcent effect. It is employed in many of the ways traditionally described as a local application to soothe inflamed skin conditions and internally for gastritis and other inflamed disorders of the digestive tract. It acts by reflex to loosen and soothe a hard, tight cough and is valuable in bronchitis. Recurrent cystitis or bladder inflammation is also relieved by Marshmallow. All in all, it is a gentle remedy with a wide range of uses; traditionally, a stick of Marshmallow root was given to teething infants to chew to ease the soreness; this could be true today, and indicates its safety.

# Marjoram

*Origanum marjorana* and *Origanum vulgare*, Labiatae

## Description

There are two species of Marjorams which have been widely used through history: the Wild Marjoram, or Oregano (*Origanum vulgare*), has a very ancient medicinal reputation, while the Sweet or Knotted Marjoram (*Origanum marjorana*) has also been employed medicinally for

Marjoram from *Commentarii in Sex Libros Pedacii Dioscoridis* by Pierandrea Matthioli, 1565.

similar problems but is best known in cookery. The picture is somewhat complicated by the widespread use of the hardier Pot Marjoram (*Origanum onites*) as a substitute in cooking. They are found growing wild in chalky soils across Europe and Asia.

Their appearances are similar, with a bush-like shape and small grey-green leaves. Wild Marjoram has flowers that stand in a pyramidal shape, reddish-pink in colour. Sweet Marjoram produces a knotty kind of growth of its flowering stems, hence the other name, and they vary from white to pink and pale mauve in colour. Both plants are covered with fine hairs, and are very aromatic — the scent of Wild Marjoram is perhaps more pungent, with a hint of thyme.

## History and Origins

The generic name *Origanum* derives from Greek and means 'Joy of the Mountains', referring to its usual habitat. The Greeks believed that Marjoram growing on graves brought peace and happiness to the departed spirits. Both they and the Romans valued Marjoram (almost certainly the Wild variety) for resisting infections and poisons, and for digestive upsets. The Romans introduced the plant to Britain, where it soon grew in drier areas.

Country folk took to Marjoram for all sorts of uses: as a source of a dye for woollen cloth, in making ale, in washbags and other perfume preparations, as a 'strewing herb' for sprinkling on the floor of rooms to make them smell nicer, and as a tea for headaches, colds, indigestion and colic, amongst other things.

Gerard mentions that: "The juyce mixed with a little milke, being poured into the eares, mitigateth the paines thereof" which Culpeper also suggests, and the latter also refers to the use of the essential oil put onto an aching tooth to relieve the pain, so an anti-inflammatory effect was noticed a long time ago.

More typical of traditional usage is Culpeper's initial description of Marjoram's benefits. He writes: "It strengthens the stomach and head much; there is scarcely a better herb growing for relieving a sour stomach, loss of appetite,

164

Marjoram *Origanum vulgare* from Woodville's
*Medical Botany*, 1790.

Although Sweet Marjoram is a perennial, it is easily affected by frost, and is generally grown as an annual in Britain — one of the reasons why the tougher Pot Marjoram is often offered for the kitchen garden. Marjorams like a dry, sunny position, and a warm, sheltered spot will give them the best prospects.

The seeds are very small, and may need to be mixed with sand for even sowing. They also take a long time to germinate, and careful weeding is often necessary to allow them room for growth. Plants can be propagated by cuttings.

## MODERN MEDICINAL USES

Marjoram is no longer frequently used in medical herbalism, although it has considerable value in head colds or 'flu, either as a hot infusion or in a steam inhalation. It has a greater popularity on the Continent, for nervous, flatulent dyspepsia or tension headaches. Both here and abroad, the external use of the oil in rheumatic or muscular pains has come to be much appreciated again. It is perhaps due for a revaluation of its properties; these overlap with other remedies of the Labiate family but the wealth of traditional experience is a good indicator of its potential.

# Mistletoe

*Viscum album*, Loranthaceae

## DESCRIPTION

Mistletoe is familiar to anyone who has celebrated Christmas. It is found throughout Europe, Asia and even northern Africa. It is a parasitic plant, growing on the branches of trees. It is spread by birds eating the berries and wiping their beaks on the tree.

It is evergreen, and bushes can be easily spotted in winter, looking like large nests high up in trees. It grows on deciduous trees, and prefers those with a soft bark, such as apple trees. The

cough, consumption of the lungs; it cleanses the body of choler, expels poison, remedies the infirmities of the spleen, and helps the bites of venomous beasts."

Of the Sweet Marjoram, Culpeper gives similar indications, saying that it "is warming and comforting in cold diseases of the head, stomach, sinews, and other parts". There is an interesting example of Marjoram's value in colds: during the Thirty Years' War, the famous leader Wallenstein was cleared of a severe head cold by the German physician von Hilden, who was very handsomely rewarded by the grateful statesman.

yellow-green stems are forked, and the leaves are rather leathery in texture, aligned in pairs. The tiny yellow flowers are either male or female, each appearing on different plants. The female flowers are succeeded by the smooth, globular, white berries. These ripen in December, and have been used a lot in the past to make birdlime, which is the meaning in old Dutch of the word 'mistle'.

### HISTORY AND ORIGINS

Mistletoe was a sacred plant for most of the ancient cultures of Europe; they considered it to be a symbol of immortality, because it stayed green and alive when the trees on which it grew were dead-looking in the depths of winter. Since it cannot be grown in the ground, it was often thought to be part of the tree, its living essence.

It features in many myths and legends: for instance, it was the 'golden bough' of the *Aeneid*, opening the way to the underworld. In Norse mythology, the beautiful and otherwise immortal god Balder was slain by an arrow made from Mistletoe; it was afterwards given into the care of the goddess of love, hence the tradition of kissing under the Mistletoe.

The most famous of the old associations of Mistletoe is with the Druids. They revered it above all other plants, and harvested it with great ceremony, sometimes even with a golden sickle. There are mentions of Druidic rites connected with Mistletoe in the writings of Ovid. Modern cartoon story-lovers will remember the druid in the Asterix stories as a gentle caricature of these beliefs.

It was used by Hippocrates as a treatment for vertigo and even epilepsy, and Mistletoe's reputation in epileptic conditions continued until very recent times. Culpeper says: "Misseltoe is a cephalic and nervine medicine, useful for convulsive fist, palsy, and vertigo."

In the Middle Ages, the Abbess Hildegarde recommended it for various chest complaints, and by the nineteenth century the Abbé Kneipp was using it for hypertension and circulatory disorders. Its relaxing effect seems to have been the main feature of its uses, quietening down convulsive movements of the limbs in epileptic attacks, nervous palpitations, etc.

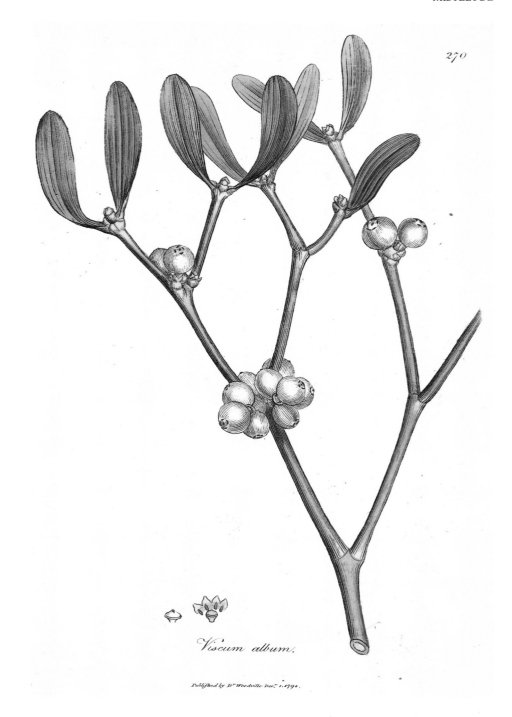

*Viscum album.*

Published by Dr Woodville Dec.r 1. 1791.

Mistletoe *Viscum album* from Woodville's *Medical Botany*, 1790.

### CULTIVATION

Mistletoe has to be grown on trees. Birds are the usual carriers, notably the thrush, which has earned it the name of 'Missel', or 'mistle thrush'. It can be done by hand, rubbing the berries on the branches of a tree, or putting them into a deliberately made nick.

### MODERN MEDICINAL USES

The leaves and twigs are the parts used medicinally, the berries are poisonous and narcotic. The actions of Mistletoe are to slow the heart rate and dilate the blood-vessels, and act as a relaxant, and this has been helpful in symptoms due to nervous tension, such as palpitations, high blood pressure and muscle spasm.

An interesting use of Mistletoe has been developed on the Continent by

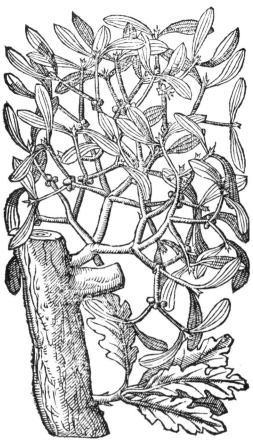

Mistletoe from Gerard's *Herball*.

anthroposophical doctors, following the ideas of Rudolph Steiner, who use a preparation of it for some kinds of cancer. In this country, it is the more usual actions described above that are used by herbalists, although less so nowadays than in earlier times.

# Mustard

*Sinapis alba* and *Sinapis nigra*, Cruciferae

## DESCRIPTION

The Mustards, black and white, are grown in many parts of the world, from America to Europe, Asia and northern Africa, and often found wild in fields and by roadsides. They are similar in appearance, the White Mustard being smaller.

Mustards are upright annuals, growing up to three or four feet in the case of the black species. *Sinapis alba* has pinnatifid leaves, while *Sinapis nigra* has linear but entire leaves. The fruits of the former lie horizontally and are covered with hairs, while Black Mustard has upright, smooth pods. The yellow flowers are cross-shaped like others in this family.

The seeds are yellowish in the White Mustard, and dark reddish-brown in the black variety; the latter are much smaller. Neither of the seeds have an aroma, unless they are mixed with water and the oil of mustard is formed.

## HISTORY AND ORIGINS

Mustard was revered by the ancient Greeks, who believed that it was discovered by the legendary father of medicine Aesculapius. They and the Romans consumed a great deal of Mustard, often pounded into wine as a digestive stimulant and tonic. Probably the Romans introduced it into England, but there is not much mention of it before the fifteenth century.

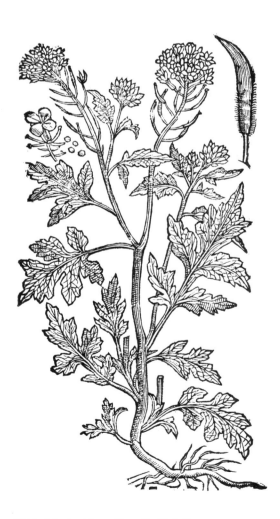

White Mustard from Gerard's *Herball*.

Shakespeare mentions the plant a few times, and the herbalist Coles describes in 1657 how Mustard seeds were ground and made up into balls with honey or vinegar to preserve them. It wasn't until the eighteenth century that a Mrs Clements of Durham created a ground mustard powder, and this was known as Durham Mustard for a long time.

As well as the seeds, the Romans ate the young leaves as a vegetable, and John Evelyn wrote at the end of the seventeenth century that: "When in the leaf, Mustard ... is of incomparable effect to quicken and revive the spirits." Animals have also been fed on Mustards, which have also been widely grown as green manures, to be ploughed in.

As usual, Culpeper has much to say about the medicinal properties of Mustard. Of the black variety he says: "It is an excellent sauce for clarifying the blood, and for weak stomachs" and has a generally stimulating and warming effect. Apart from internal medication, Mustard seeds were highly rated for local application for aches and pains. Culpeper describes them: "Poultices made with Mustard-flower, crumbs of bread, and vinegar, are frequently applied to the soles of the feet in fevers, and maybe used to advantage in old rheumatic and sciatic pains."

Mustard poultices and plasters have been thus used down the centuries as a counter-irritant to relieve inner inflammation and congestion. The *British Pharmacopoeia* has listed Compound Liniment of Mustard for a long time, and older people especially can remember using them and having Mustard footbaths for chilblains or poor circulation.

## CULTIVATION

The seeds are sown in spring; they grow best in rich soil, two traditionally popular areas in this country being Gloucestershire ("Best Tewkesbury", as Evelyn described it) and Yorkshire. The crop can be spoilt by wet weather; the seeds shoul be collected in early autumn and dried. Mustard seeds retain their vitality for a

Opposite: Black and White Mustard *Sinapis nigra* and *S. alba* from *Hortus Medicus* by George Graves, 1834.

Pl.35.

Pl.34.

S. alba.

Sinapis nigra.

W.H.Lizars sculp!

long time, so avoid letting the plants self-sow if possible, or it will be difficult to get rid of them.

If there are diseased brassicas in the vegetable garden, make sure that all Mustard plants are removed as well, or they may harbour the disease. White Mustard seeds are usually the ones grown with cress, and they may be germinated under glass all year round — school children are aware of their ability to germinate even on blotting paper.

## MODERN MEDICINAL USES

Mustard is not nowadays used much medicinally, although the external plasters, foot-baths and so on are occasionally recommended, and are certainly effective in relieving internal inflammation. As a food, it can be valuable to stimulate the digestion, if there is no gastric inflammation; large doses are laxative.

# Nettle

*Urtica dioica*, Urticaceae

## DESCRIPTION

The common stinging nettle is found almost everywhere in the temperate regions, from America and Europe to Asia, Australia and southern Africa. They are very well known, with dark-green, finely toothed leaves and stems covered with hairs that give a sharp sting. The greenish flowers are either male or female, usually on different plants.

Nettles can grow to a height of some four feet; the annual *Urtica urens*, which is also used medicinally, is smaller and lacks the large, creeping rootstock of the perennial species. Because of these extensive roots, the latter is very difficult to eradicate. Nettles are often found on wasteland, around compost heaps and in neglected gardens, but can spring up almost anywhere!

Nettle *Urtica dioica* from Woodville's *Medical Botany*, 1790.

## HISTORY AND ORIGINS

Nettles have followed human settlements and migrations for thousands of years, and may have been brought to this country by the Romans. They certainly used them; finding a damp, cold country without their native Mediterranean warmth, the soldiers often suffered from rheumatic problems and poor circulation. They would gather bunches of Nettles and rub them into their joints, to stimulate the circulation — a rather drastic but effective measure unlikely to be followed by many people today!

The young shoots were gathered by country-folk in spring and cooked as a vegetable, and there are many recipes for Nettle soup, or 'pudding'. They need some flavouring, but are still eaten today for their vitamin and mineral content, the tea being a traditional tonic for the same

146

*Urtica dioica*

Published by Dr Woodville June 1, 1792.

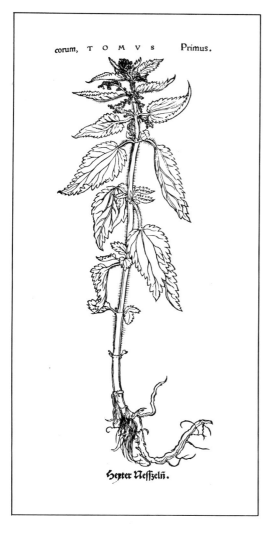

corum, T O M V S  Primus.

heyter Ueffzelñ.

Nettles *Herbarium Vivae Eicones* by Otto Brunfels, 1537.

reasons. Another way of using the young tops was to make Nettle beer, and again there are recipes still in use. I can vouch for its flavour, and its potency!

The fibres of Nettles make a very fine thread, and at times they have been used for cloth-making. The eighteenth-century poet Campbell described travelling through Scotland, where: "I have eaten nettles, I have slept in nettle sheets, and I have dined off a nettle tablecloth." During World War I, the Germans were unable to obtain adequate supplies of cotton, and many of their uniforms contained Nettle cloth.

The medicinal properties of Nettles rely to some extent on their iron and Vitamin C content, amongst other constituents, and they were one of the most valued spring tonics following a re-stricted diet over winter. Culpeper describes this eloquently: "It consumes the phlegmatic superfluities in the body of man, that the coldness and moisture of winter has left behind."

Nettles are one of the herbs called in older herbals as 'alteratives', or blood-cleansers. The thirteenth-century Physicians of Myddfai suggested taking a Nettle drink twice a day, to "cure you of the jaundice, renovate the blood, and remove any disease existing therein". At different times, for example in Paris in the mid-eighteenth century, it has been fashionable as a tea, and Nettle teabags are quite widely available again now.

### CULTIVATION

Nettles grow so easily that it is hardly necessary to cultivate them; they like a fair amount of nitrogen, and are a sign of a rich soil, which they rob of its minerals. The young shoots in spring are less bitter than older plants, and it is possible to get a couple of cuts of a patch of Nettles for food or drinks. When boiled, or if boiling water is poured onto them, or else if they are thoroughly dried, they lose their sting completely.

### MODERN MEDICINAL USES

Nettles are a considerable storehouse of nutrients, and this alone makes them valuable in a number of conditions. They additionally have diuretic effects, stimulate the circulation and have an effect on lowering blood sugar levels. They are frequently prescribed in skin disorders where there is poor circulation and/or a debilitated state. Other conditions for which they may help include late-onset diabetes where insulin is not needed, lack of breast-milk in mothers, and iron-deficiency anaemia.

## Peppermint

*Mentha piperita*, Labiatae

### DESCRIPTION

Peppermint is actually a hybrid from wild species, especially water mint and gar-den mint. There are two varieties, Black Peppermint and White Peppermint. They are found through America and Europe in damp places, probably as garden escapes from long ago,

Both varieties have a characteristic mint appearance, with branching, upright, square stems and lanceolate leaves with finely toothed margins. In the black variety, the leaves have a purplish tinge and the stems are dark red, while the smaller and more slender white variety has green, coarser leaves and green stems.

The flowers are purple and appear in whorls in the axils of the upper leaves. The plant is sterile and propagates by its runners, which run just above or just below the soil. The best distinguishing feature from other mints is probably the peppermint aroma; this is stronger in the black variety (*Mentha piperita 'piperita'*) than in the white (*Mentha piperita officinalis'*).

Other useful species are the Garden or Spearmint, *Mentha viridis*, and Penny-royal, *Mentha pulegium*. There are a number of other mints that can be grown in the garden, but those above have had a long history of medicinal uses.

### HISTORY AND ORIGINS

The Greeks, Romans and ancient Egyptians all have records of using mints; it is not easy to say whether this was actually Peppermint, but the properties of spearmint and true Peppermint are similar. Certainly, the Romans used mints a great deal in their cooking, flavouring sauces and even wines with them. The Greeks employed mint to scent their baths and as a perfume; they allocated different parts of the body to different scents, and mint was reserved for the arms!

All the medieval herbals describe the virtues of mints, showing how widely they were used. The Pilgrim Fathers took mint to America, whence it quickly spread as an escape. Although Peppermint was probably around long before this time, and it is mentioned by Culpeper and others, the first true botanical recognition of it as a separate species was not until the seventeenth century. From that time on it very quickly became included in the *British Pharmacopoeia*, and

Pl. 43.

*Mentha piperita.*

has been highly valued and widely used since.

Traditional medicinal applications of Peppermint are thus intermingled with those for spearmint; of the latter, Culpeper for instance lists some forty uses. He does enter Peppermint separately, with this description: "This herb has a strong, agreeable, aromatic smell, and a moderate warm bitterish taste; it is useful for complaints of the stomach, such as wind, vomiting &c. for which there are few remedies of greater efficacy."

Of both spearmint and Peppermint he has this to say: "Their fragrance betokens them cephalics; they effectually take off nauseousness and retchings to vomit; they are also of use in looseness".

Of European countries, England was considered to grow the finest Peppermint, and a large acreage was devoted to its production, especially around Mitcham in Surrey, from the late eighteenth century. Mrs Grieve describes in detail the various cultivation centres around Europe and America at the turn of this century, and shows a clear picture of large-scale growing and oil extraction.

## CULTIVATION

Like other mints, Peppermint runners can spread fairly rapidly, and they are best grown in a border separate from other herbs. As mentioned, propagation is exclusively by dividing runners. Planting runners, with roots, into a rich, moist soil in spring or autumn is all that is required. They prefer a warm, rather sheltered spot, but some shade is essential to avoid drying out the ground or evaporating the volatile oil.

The main problem with Peppermint and other species is mint rust, a fungal disease. Constantly renewing the plants may help to overcome this disease; it is not supposed to affect the underground parts of the plants. In any case, harvesting the leaves involves cutting down to the roots; mints should ideally never be allowed to run to seed.

Opposite: Peppermint *Mentha piperita* from Woodville's *Medical Botany*, 1790.

## MODERN MEDICINAL USES

Oil of Peppermint is the most widely used volatile oil in medicine, and often features in conventional medications for flatulent dyspepsia. A simple home remedy, popular for centuries, for indigestion, flatulence, colic and/or nausea is Peppermint tea made from the leaves.

Medical herbalists frequently prescribe Peppermint for these problems, and also recommend it for feverish colds and 'flu, since it is a good inducer of sweating and so cools down the hot, restless sufferer.

# Rose

*Rosa gallica*, Rosaceae

## DESCRIPTION

Rosa gallica, the Apothecary's Rose, is one of the oldest varieties of rose in existence, being cultivated by the Greeks and Romans, and pure examples of it are difficult to obtain as there have been so many hybrids over the centuries. The Rose is thought to originate from Persia, and spread from there to southern Europe; now, of course, roses are grown everywhere.

The word *rosa* comes from the ancient Greek *rodon*, meaning red, and *Rosa gallica* is a deep crimson, with a fine perfume. The stems are quite prickly, and the leaves have fine hairs. Other notable roses from the past with a medicinal/perfumery reputation are the paler coloured *Rosa damascena*, the Damask rose, and *Rosa centifolia*, the Cabbage rose. Much use is and has been made by herbalists of the hips of the Dog rose, *Rosa canina*, as a source of Vitamin C and as an astringent.

## HISTORY AND ORIGINS

Roses have been used since the dawn of time, and are probably the first flowers to have been cultivated. *Rosa gallica*, also sometimes called the Province rose, has been the subject of countless poems, books and legends through many cultures and lands. The scent was considered by the Egyptians as reserved for

Rose from Gerard's *Herball*.

the pharaohs, and the tomb of Tutenkhamun contained bunches of them, still faintly aromatic after three thousand years.

The Romans took to roses with great gusto; they used them as decorations, for strewing on the floor or in the path of victorious war-chariots, for crowning brides at weddings (hence the origin of confetti) and for scenting their baths. They also incorporated them into food and drink, for instance floating petals in cups of wine, in jams, cakes and other confections. They chewed pastilles made from roses to sweeten their breath, and applied rose oil to their skin.

While the Romans used infused oils of roses, it was not until the tenth century AD that Arab physicians started distilling the essential oil from the flowers, and using it in medicine and perfumery. There is a story that the oil, or Attar of Roses, was discovered at a wedding feast of one of the Moguls when a canal surrounding the party was filled with

*Rosa gallica*

Published by D.<sup>r</sup> Woodville May 1. 1792.

roses; as the sun warmed the water, the essential oil separated and floated on the surface; the bridal couple ran their hands through the oil and discovered its intense perfume.

The Rose has been a symbol of love from ancient times, dedicated to Venus and Cupid. It has also been a sign of confidentiality, and a rose would be suspended over a table where secret discussions took place. Even today, we have a plaster rose in the centre of many a ceiling as a remnant of this practice. They feature in several coats of arms and insignia, for instance the Houses of York and Lancaster at the time of the Wars of the Roses.

Medicinally, the red *Rosa gallica* was considered to be the best species to use, having a strongly astringent effect. The famous Arab physician Avicenna rated it highly, using it for tuberculosis and spitting of blood. Gerard gives a full description of many kinds of rose which he grew in his garden, and says: "The distilled water of Roses is good for strengthening of the heart, and refreshing of the spirits, and likewise for all things that require a gentle cooling".

Culpeper too has a lot to say about the different roses; of the red rose he states: "This binds more and is more restringent than any of the other species, good against all kind of fluxes; it strengthens the stomach, prevents vomiting, stops tickling coughs … and is of service in consumption."

The *British Pharmacopoeia*, among others, recommended only *Rosa gallica* for making rose-water preparations as a gentle astringent for external use, as well as a syrup to flavour other medicines and act as an astringent. In France, there is a more widespread tradition of using roses in folk medicine, as well as the famous perfumery industry, and Messegue enthuses about Province roses to ease a sore throat, diarrhoea and the like, and as a tonic to the lungs. He also recommends using strongly rose-scented baths as a treatment for rheumatism.

Opposite: Officinal Rose *Rosa gallica* from Woodville's *Medical Botany*, 1790.

Dog Rose *Rosa canina* from Leonhart Fuchs's *De Historia Stirpium*, 1542.

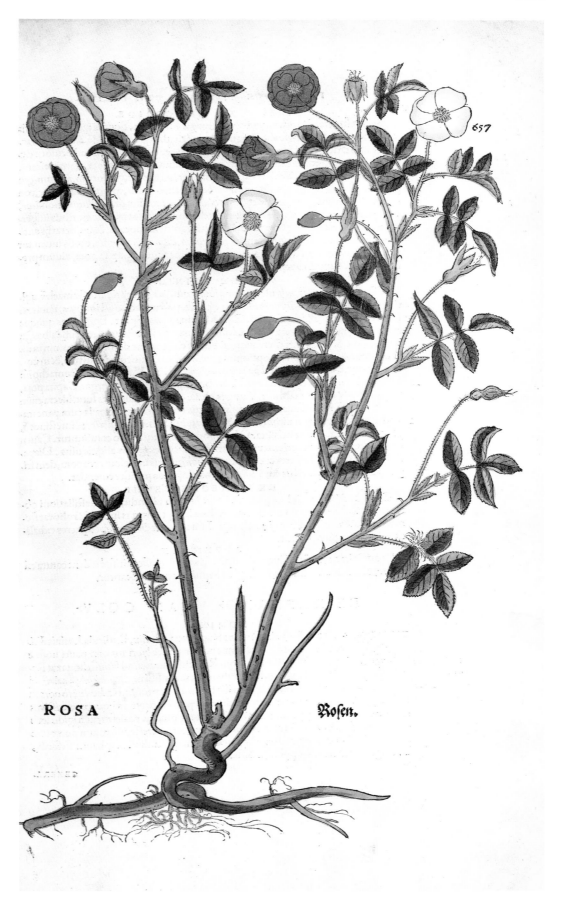

ROSA      Roſen.

657

## CULTIVATION

There are so many books and articles on growing and pruning roses that it is superfluous to describe it in detail. Roses generally like a well-worked and rich soil, and many old gardeners increased the aroma and vigour of their plants with a dressing of horse manure. The flower-buds are collected just as they open for the preparation of syrups, etc, and the distillation of oil.

## MODERN MEDICINAL USES

Roses are not really used medicinally any more, although rosewater is a valuable local remedy where a soothing astringent is needed. The syrup or infusion can certainly help with sore throats and the like, and the essential oil is extensively used in aromatherapy for its calming effects as well as benefits for the skin.

# Rosemary

*Rosmarinus officinalis*, Labiatae

## DESCRIPTION

A native of southern Europe, Rosemary is nevertheless reasonably hardy, and grows quite well in Britain and America if not in too exposed a position. It is an evergreen shrub, growing to four feet or so if left untended. The narrow, linear leaves are a dark green on the upper surface and a pale, silver-grey underneath. They curve slightly, like pine needles.

There are different varieties, with differing habits of growth; for instance, 'Miss Jessup's Upright' has a compact, erect appearance, whilst some types are completely prostrate. Usually, Rosemary is a rather straggly bush. The flowers are a pretty pale blue, in clusters in the axils, and in a mild winter they can appear as early as January.

The whole plant gives off a strong, characteristic aroma, almost reminiscent of camphor. It is this volatile oil that carries most of the medicinal properties.

Rosemary *Rosmarinus officinalis* from *Getreue Darstellung…Arzneykunde*, F.G. Haynes 1821.

## HISTORY AND ORIGINS

Rosemary was held in high regard by the ancient Egyptians and Greeks, symbolizing remembrance and also fidelity. The pharaohs had sprigs of Rosemary placed in their tombs to help them recall their former life during the journey to the next. These attributions meant that Rosemary was in great demand for weddings, religious ceremonies and funerals.

The scent of Rosemary has a piercing, stimulating quality which was thought to be particularly helpful to scholars, to aid concentration and memory. The prize students were given wreaths of Rosemary to wear, rather like the wreaths of laurel awarded to the best athletes. Shakespeare was well aware of all these attributes, Ophelia choosing "Rosemary for remembrance" as she contemplates death.

In the Middle Ages, Rosemary enjoyed a tremendous boost in popularity with its use in Hungary Water, an external application for rheumatic limbs. It was believed to have been invented for Queen Elizabeth of Hungary in the thirteenth century, who was crippled with gout and rheumatism; such was the revival in her health and appearance that the King of Poland proposed marriage! The preparation was famed throughout Europe for centuries, and is mentioned by all the medieval writers.

The Physicians of Myddfai, practising at the same time as the creation of Hungary Water, used Rosemary as a general tonic, devoting pages of writing to the description of its virtues. Gerard quoted the old Arab herbalists in recommending Rosemary to "comfort the brain, the memory and the inward senses", while Culpeper says that among other virtues it "helps a weak memory, and quickens the senses".

Alongside Juniper and Lavender, Rosemary was burnt in French hospitals to fumigate the wards and kill off airborne infections. It also forms part of the traditional posy given to Judges, to "sweeten the pestilential airs" in the crowded courtrooms of the past.

## CULTIVATION

Rosemary survives best in a light, dry soil. It can be quite sandy, but some underlying chalk is helpful because it needs lime; crushed egg-shells can be used to provide this. Plenty of sunshine is needed to allow the maximum of oil to be produced.

Rosemary can be grown from seed, although they are difficult to germinate, but cuttings in early spring or after flowering are quite easy to root. Division of the roots is also possible, every two or three years, and simply layering the bush by pegging lower branches under a little soil can be successful.

## MODERN MEDICINAL USES

Rosemary is a stimulant to the circulation and a tonic to the nervous system, and is excellent in nervous exhaustion. Its long reputation for relieving headaches and migraines is well justified, especially

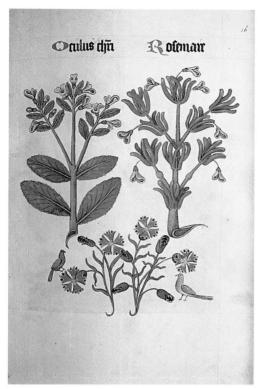

Rosemary from *The Herbal and Bestiary* England, c. 1510—20.

when there is a background of exhaustion or even depression and the headaches tend to be relieved by warmth to the head. As a liver tonic and digestive stimulant it is very helpful in bilious headaches or simply a weak digestion.

Externally, Rosemary is a rubefacient, stimulating local circulation and reducing the need for internal inflammation. This can be used in rheumatic complaints, also to aid blood flow to the scalp in conditions of hair loss or dandruff.

# Sage

*Salvia officinalis*, Labiatae

## DESCRIPTION

Sage is a native of the Mediterranean region, but has been cultivated for centuries all over the world. It is a shrubby plant, growing to some two or three feet, with stems that get increasingly woody with age.

It is perennial, growing new branches from the woody base each year. The leaves are softly hairy, with a leathery feel. They are stalked, an inch or so long, oblong and grey-green in colour, with fine veins. The variety considered finest for medicinal purposes is often called Red or Purple Sage, and the leaves are accordingly a purplish colour.

The flowers are violet-blue, and appear in whorls during July. The plant has a strong, highly distinctive aroma. There is a broad-leaved and a narrow-leaved variety of Sage; these are classed, like the Red Sage, as variations of *Salvia officinalis*, not as a separate species.

## HISTORY AND ORIGINS

The Latin name comes from the word *salvere*, to save or heal, and it was regarded as one of the most important remedies in ancient times. There was an old saying, "How can a man die when he has Sage in his garden?" which highlights this reputation. (The question was answered by saying that no herb can defeat death, but it made its point!)

The Greek writer and physician, Dioscorides, recommended it for such varied complaints as fevers, urinary stones and irregular periods. In the twelfth century, the Abbess Hildegarde believed it was a universal remedy, listing many ailments where it was useful.

In the sixteenth century, Gerard grew several varieties in his garden, and advised it for nervous disorders, the palsy and so forth. Culpeper too thought it was "warming and quickening" to the senses, but particularly prescribed it to bring on menstruation, or else to increase urination. Externally, he suggested all manner of applications, such as rheumatic aches, pains, wounds and sores.

Its antiseptic effects were put to the test by the grave-robbers in Toulouse in the plague of 1630, who smeared themselves with the original 'Four Thieves' Vinegar', consisting of Sage with Thyme, Lavender and Rosemary. The more famous version used later in Marseilles relied heavily on Garlic as the prime ingredient, but Sage had proved its worth.

Before we had good supplies of China tea, Sage tea was the closest thing to a national drink; indeed, the Chinese themselves preferred it to their own tea when the Dutch began bartering with

Herbā absinthiū inaceto decoctū œ inductū panno inpone
sicorp' tenerū fuerit œ melle ipone. adlumbricos.
Herbe absinthiū œ marrubii 7 lupinoꝛ. parā pondā iaꝗ mulsa
cocta l'inuino austeri iposita iumbilico necat lūbcos. adingu
ina l'inter trigines molestaſ. Herbe absinthiū surculū
sumito œ isemiunctum tecum portato. Hoīa Salute.

Greci Lelisfacon · Cassion.
Bechion · Cilisfacos.
Sfagnos. Egiptū dnus.
Pphe ꝰ ua · latini Salui a
tuisi lagine. Cor saluium.
Elelisticon aꝗ ſtuis ꝗuioris
œ odoris usualis ū ꝗ ē bo
ni odoris aclenioris sal
uia uocat. Est ꝗ frutex si
ue sarmitū longitudine
poritectū sub al bidū uir
gis maioribꝫ 7 ꝗ dratis cū
foliis paulo asꝑis odoris bo
ni. œ fruct' siue semine in
sūmitate ramoꝛ similior
sh · nascitur iaſpis locis œ ē
darguentis cū acmonia. ꝗ de
sepe uenenū eic. ad ure t pru
Herba saluia deuoꝗtū œ de ea aꝗ
trū. ad pruriginē circa anum
deuoꝗtur œ de ea aꝗ isteriores par
œ sedat pruriginē sūme. Homina
dron · Corion · coriandri ·

minoꝛ aꝗ
uirtutis re
niqꝫ pdictano
riginem.
inficas uere
Herba saluia
tes sūmitē
Greci Corian

them. Sage has been used in cooking for a long time, and the aroma is immediately reminiscent of stuffing — in the past its antiseptic qualities helped to preserve diners from the potentially dangerous meats.

Its astringent properties have been used to treat throat infections, mainly using the tincture, and this has been listed in the *Pharmacopoeia* of several countries, especially the USA. The tea is a traditional folk remedy for people under stress, acting as a stimulant and tonic.

## CULTIVATION

Sage will grow in most situations, being quite hardy and resistant to diseases. It does best on a light, dry soil in a warm position, as in its native regions.

If a flowering variety, mostly the narrow-leaved Sage, it can be propagated

Great Sage from Gerard's *Herball*.

Opposite: Sage from a twelfth-century copy of *Herbarium of Apuleius*.

*Salvia officinalis*

Published by D.ʳ Woodville August 1.1790.

Sage *Salvia officinalis* from Woodville's *Medical Botany*, 1790.

from seeds, of which it will produce masses. Otherwise, Red and broad-leaved Garden Sage are usually propagated by either layering or cuttings, taken with a 'heel' in late spring. Sage plants get very woody and straggly by the time they are five years old, and replacing them regularly helps to keep young, vigorous plants.

## MODERN MEDICINAL USES

The astringent and healing qualities of Sage are very useful in mouth and throat problems, tonsillitis, etc. As a gargle, the tincture is best, and commercial preparations are widely available. It is a stimulant to digestion and circulation, yet has the capacity to reduce excessive sweating. This, combined with an oestrogenic effect, is often used nowadays to aid women having difficulties during the menopause.

This last property means that Sage should be avoided in pregnancy without expert advice, and used carefully as a domestic remedy anyway; gargles/mouthwashes are its best first aid uses. Professionally, Sage can be a valuable tonic in debility and convalescence from illness, among the other indications mentioned.

# St John's Wort

*Hypericum perforatum*, Hypericaceae

## DESCRIPTION

St John's Wort is an upright, herbaceous perennial found growing wild throughout Europe, America and Asia. It is mainly found on roadsides, open woodland and dry banks. It will grow to some two feet, with erect, many-branched brown stems.

The small, oblong leaves contain tiny, translucent oil glands, and if a leaf is held up to the light they can be seen looking like lots of pin-prick perforations, hence the specific name. The bright yellow, star-like flowers cover the plant in midsummer, followed by small, round black seeds. These give off a resinous smell, the name *Hypericum* referring to a belief that the herb's unpleasant aroma would deter evil spirits.

## HISTORY AND ORIGINS

The plant was so called because it was believed to bloom on June 24th, St John's Day, and the perforated leaves have led to many legends concerning its benefits in wounds. Interestingly, the flowers (and leaves) infused in oil for some time produce a red oil that is very helpful in treating wounds and other skin problems.

Gerard gives the classic description of this, claiming his oil was unsurpassed for wounds: the flowers and leaves, "stamped, and put into a glasse with oile olive, and set in the hot sun for certain weeks together, and then strained from

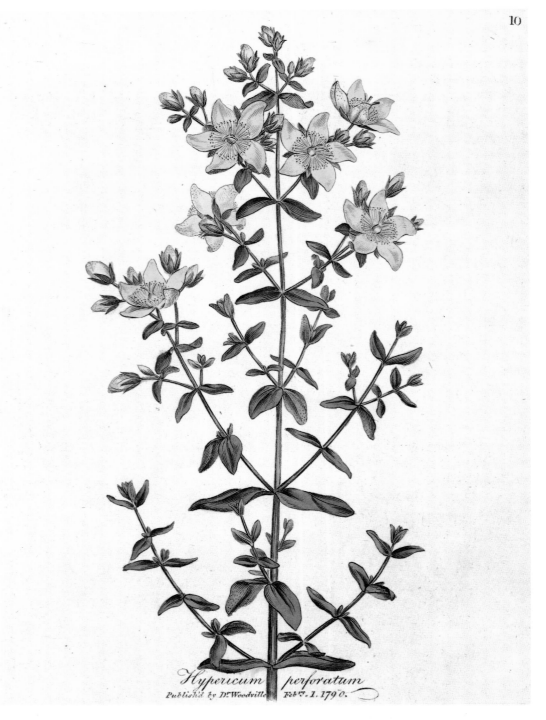

St John's Wort *Hypericum perforatum* from Woodville's *Medical Botany*, 1790.

those herbs, and the like quantitie of new put in and sunned in like manner, doth make an oile of the colour of bloud, which is a most pretious remedie for deep wounds".

Possibly due to the lessening of infected wounds, from sword fights and the like, St John's Wort became less well known and used in the eighteenth and nineteenth centuries. The Abbé Kneipp wrote in 1891: "St John's Wort was once called the 'fairy herb' because of its efficacy. Nowadays we have entirely forgotten it and the services it can render." It is now, however, more widely used by herbalists, with modern research highlighting internal uses as well as the traditional oil applications.

## CULTIVATION

Since it grows so well as a wild plant, often seen as a weed of wasteland, St John's Wort presents few problems for cultivation. It will seed itself around the garden if left unchecked, and this is the easiest way to propagate it. Choose a dry, open site if possible, although it will tolerate partial shade. To make the oil, collect the flowers just as they become fully open, on a sunny morning after the dew has evaporated.

## MODERN MEDICINAL USES

Internally, St John's Wort has a relaxing and calming effect, and in modern herbal medicine is frequently prescribed as a natural antidepressant in chronic anxiety states. In any situation of long-term stress leading to fatigue and depression, whether from emotional worries, work strains or, for example, the irritability associated with the menopause for some

St John's Wort from Gerard's *Herball*.

women, St John's Wort acts as a gentle nervous restorative.

The red oil is a valuable application for wounds, mild burns, rheumatic pains, neuralgia, sciatica, and so on. In Russia doctors have used the oil with success on radiation burns, so we are still discovering new uses for its soothing and healing properties.

# Scullcap

*Scutellaria lateriflora*, Labiatae

## DESCRIPTION

This species of Scullcap is a native of eastern America, where it has been known as Mad-Dog, or Virginian, Scullcap. It is a perennial, reaching two or three feet in height. It is very difficult to obtain in dried form in Britain, with substitutions by other Scullcaps very common. There is some botanical confusion over closely related species, to add to the difficulty. *Scutellaria galericulata*, which grows widely in temperate zones, including Britain, has been used medicinally as it has similar properties.

The ovate leaves come in opposite pairs, and the small blue, helmet-shaped flowers appear in one-sided racemes, hence the specific name.

## HISTORY AND ORIGINS

Scullcap has a relatively short history in herbal medicine, only a few centuries (!), although Indian use may be far longer. Scullcap was one of the herbs that was used to illustrate the 'Doctrine of Signatures'.

Since the helmet-like upper lip of the Scullcap flower was thought to resemble the headgear of the same name, it was believed that this 'signature' showed it should be used for head-related problems. It did indeed have a high reputation as a nervine, for anxiety states, even epilepsy, and so this belief was confirmed. Originally, this idea probably came from plants with known virtues, like Scullcap, but it fell into disrepute by the eighteenth century since the 'reading' of the signature depended

on the individual not on any true medicinal actions.

The nickname Mad-Dog Scullcap came from a traditional reputation it gained as a cure for hydrophobia. It has been used for treating convulsions and St Vitus' Dance, and was seriously considered in the nineteenth century as a remedy for epilepsy. Interestingly, overdosage led to giddiness and muscular twitching, which suggested that lower, if not homoeopathic, doses are most effective.

## CULTIVATION

Scullcap grows in wet, marshy ground near rivers, and the English species too prefers to grow by water. In the garden, they will do quite well in an open border, and do not thrive in rich soil. Propagation is most commonly done from seed, sown in spring, in gentle heat if possible. The plants may be transplanted in the autumn. *Scutellaria galericulata* especially has a spreading habit, only reaching some eightteen inches high.

## MODERN MEDICINAL USES

As a relaxant to the central nervous system, Scullcap has wide applications in anxiety, stress and nervous exhaustion. In the dosage ranges used by herbal practitioners, it has no overt sedative effects, and acts as a restorative to nerve functioning alongside its relaxing, antispasmodic properties. It can help to reduce the severity of epileptic attacks, but professional treatment is necessary.

# Senna

*Cassia senna* and *Cassia angustifolia*, Leguminosae

## DESCRIPTION

There are two main species used as Senna, Alexandrian and Tinnevelly originating from respectively Sudan and Saudi Arabia, but they are very similar in appearance and activity. Senna is also cultivated elsewhere, notably in India.

Senna is a small shrub, only two or three feet high, with spreading, pale-

162

*Cassia Senna*

*Published by Dr Woodville Sep 1.1792*

Senna *Cassia senna* from Woodville's *Medical Botany*, 1790.

green branches carrying yellowish-green pinnate leaves. These come in arrangements of four or five pairs of narrow, lanceolate leaflets, veined on the underneath. The small, yellow flowers at the tips of the stems give way to the seed pods mostly used in medicine (although the leaves have a similar action).

### History and Origins

The word Senna is an Arabic one, and it was Arab physicians like Serapion who first described its uses as a purgative. The Greeks picked up on this and it was they who preferred the pods to the more irritantly laxative leaves.

The powerful effects of Senna have often caused griping in high dosage, and over the centuries many compound preparations were developed to alleviate this side-effect. Typical mixtures included ginger, cloves, cinnamon or other carminatives to reduce the colicky spasms. At one time, the term 'black draught' was used for some of these mixtures, but since pharmacists had difficulty in deciphering the prescription and sometimes dispensed 'black drop', an opium preparation, with fatal consequences, the name was quickly done away with!

In the seventeenth century, there are records of attempts to grow Senna in hot-beds in this country. Despite flowering under these conditions they rarely developed seed pods. Since then, crops have been grown in several Middle Eastern countries, such as Egypt and Jordan.

Senna has remained in the *British Pharmacopoeia*, and is one of the best-known of herbal medicines that can be bought from pharmacists. Many people have unpleasant memories of being dosed with Senna as children to clear constipation — not a practice to be recommended generally!

### Cultivation

Senna is not suitable for growing here, and dried products will be the way that it is used. On its own, it has a sweetish, slightly nauseating taste, which is often disguised with other herbs.

### Modern Medicinal Uses

The action of Senna as a stimulating purgative has been known for centuries, and it is prescribed for atonic constipation, where the bowel muscles are flaccid and inactive. The approach of herbalists is to be as gentle as possible, and if Senna is used it is for as short a time as possible. It should *not* be used where there is tension or spasm causing the constipation, and in any case the causes for the problem will be sought. About four pods will usually be enough, preferably with a carminative such as ginger or fennel, in a tea.

Opposite: Thyme *Thymus vulgaris* from *Getreue Darstellung …Arzneykunde …*, F.G. Haynes 1830.

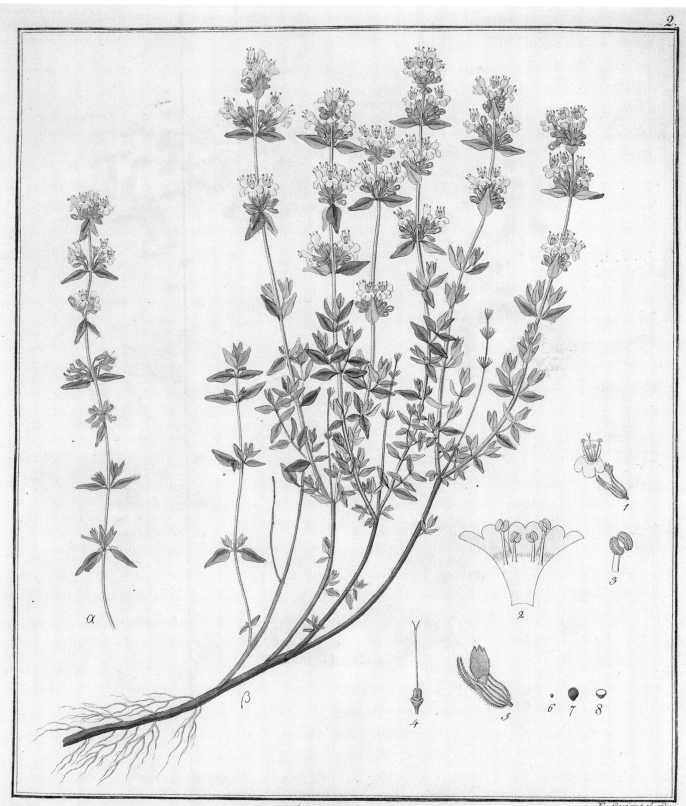

F. Guimpel fec.

*Thymus vulgaris.*

# Thyme

*Thymus vulgaris*, Labiatae

## DESCRIPTION

Thyme is indigenous to the southern European countries bordering the Mediterranean, but is cultivated throughout the world. It is closely related to the Wild, or Creeping Thyme, *Thymus serpyllum*, and both have been used medicinally for centuries.

Thyme is a perennial low-growing plant, reaching a foot in height at most. The roots are woody and fibrous, and the stems are also woody, with lots of branches. The tiny, narrow, greenish-grey leaves appear in opposite pairs, with a pair of minute leaflets at the base of the stalk.

The flowers appear in whorls in the upper leaf axils, varying in colour from pale pink to violet. The seeds are round and so small that it takes around 150,000 to make an ounce! The plant has a distinctive, pungent, aromatic smell. There are several garden varieties, with flower colours ranging from white to purple, variegated leaves and so on. A commonly grown variety is Lemon Thyme, with a fresh lemony fragrance; I have personally grown 24 different thymes, and they can all be used in cooking, teas, etc.

## HISTORY AND ORIGINS

The name Thyme is believed to derive from the Greek term meaning 'to fumigate', the Greeks using it for incense as well as medicinally. Dioscorides and Theophrastus both describe the virtues of Thyme in reducing intestinal spasms, fighting infections and improving digestion. Pliny said that burning Thyme put to flight all venomous creatures.

Thyme has been used in sachets to preserve linen from moths, and on a more gruesome note it was an ingredient in embalming preparations. Over the centuries, it acquired a reputation as a symbol of bravery, partly because of its use as a cordial to lift the spirits. In medieval times, ladies embroidered a bee hovering over a sprig of Thyme on the scarves they gave to their knights to wear as favours.

Thyme has inspired many poets over the years; Shakespeare's *A Midsummer Night's Dream*, the play which is richest in herbal lore, carries the famous lines beginning, "I know a bank whereon the wild thyme blows", and many others have alluded to it since. In the days of Charlemagne, it was obligatory to grow Thyme in the garden.

Thyme has of course acquired a considerable reputation in cooking, giving a pungent flavour to many dishes. The Romans used it to flavour cheese. For centuries Thyme was considered to produce one of the finest honeys — the Wild Thyme growing on Mount Hymettus near Athens was a famous source.

The medicinal properties of Thyme have been equally valued. Gerard grew it profusely, and Culpeper has this to say about its virtues: "It purges the body of phlegm, and is an excellent remedy for the shortness of breath. The herb taken inwardly, comforts the stomach much, and expels wind." He especially recommends it for whooping cough.

## CULTIVATION

Thyme can be grown quite easily, tolerating a range of situations, though it is only really happy on a light, dry soil in a fairly sunny position. It makes an excellent edging plant for a herb border, and can be grown as a rock plant.

Thyme will self-seed, and can be propagated this way. Otherwise, it is normally grown from cuttings taken in late spring, or by division of the plants. After a few years Thyme plants can get straggly, and regular replacement will keep a better appearance.

## MODERN MEDICINAL USES

Common Thyme and Wild Thyme have slightly different properties, but have been used in similar ways traditionally. The volatile oil, and especially its thymol content, is a powerful antiseptic, and can be use in inhalations and the like for respiratory infections. As a tincture, Thyme makes a very good gargle and mouthwash for conditions like mouth ulcers, sore throats, tonsillitis, etc.

Internally, Thyme is useful in treating digestive infections or inflammation, and will strengthen a weak digestion. It is also an expectorant, soothing and loosening a hard, dry cough in a variety of bronchial problems. It will relieve the spasms that can accompany bouts of coughing, for instance in whooping cough or bronchial asthma.

# Valerian

*Valeriana officinalis*, Valerianaceae

## DESCRIPTION

Valerian is found growing through Europe, northern Asia and America, almost up to the Arctic Circle. It is a tall perennial, growing to some four feet in height, and belongs to a widely distributed genus of plants. It grows in marshy ground, on the banks of rivers and streams.

The rootstock is short and thick, with runners extending outwards. It may take the plant a few years to develop the roots to the point where it will produce a flowering stem. The pinnate leaves have lanceolate pairs of leaflets, with indented margins.

The erect, flowering stem is fluted and hollow, and the flowers develop into a flat cluster, or cyme, white tinged with pink. They give off an unusual odour; the fresh roots are odourless, but on drying they develop the distinctive, highly pungent aroma that has been likened to cat pee! Valerian should not be confused with Red Valerian, *Centranthus rubra*, which can be seen growing on dry-stone walls in Cornwall, the Cotswolds and elsewhere.

## HISTORY AND ORIGINS

Valerian gained such a powerful medicinal reputation in olden times that it was called All-Heal, or Setwall. The Latin name probably comes from the word *valere*, to be in health. More prosaically, it

Opposite: Valerian *Valeriana officinalis* from *Hortus Medicus* by George Graves, 1834.

Pl. 15.

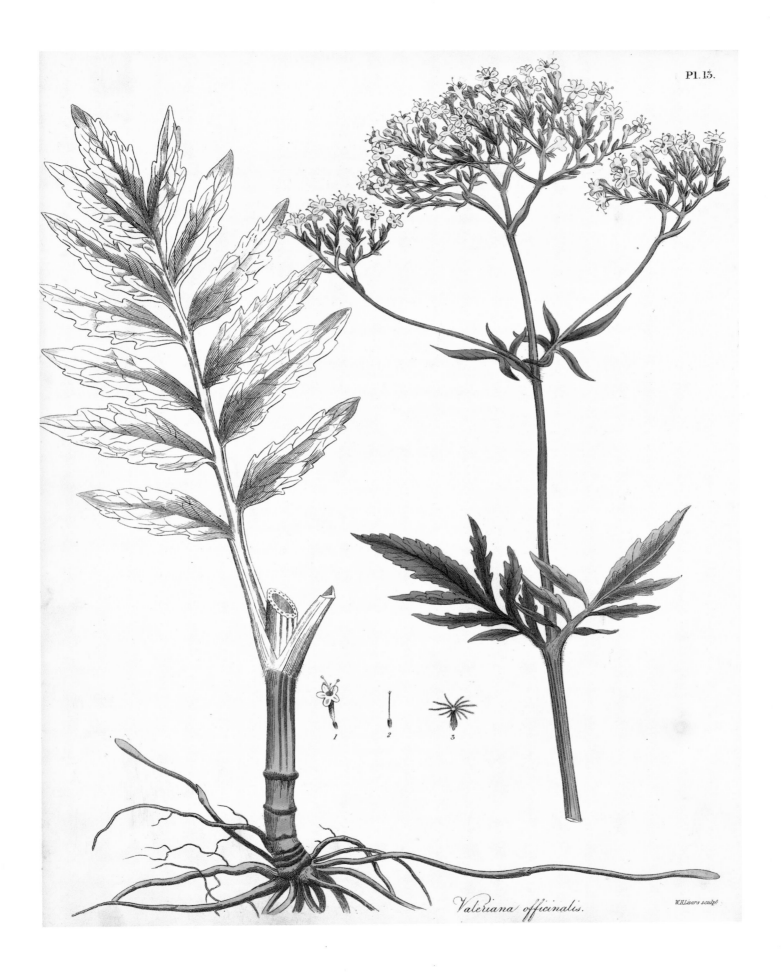

*Valeriana officinalis.*

W.H.Lizars sculpt

was known to the ancients as *Phu*, or *Fu*, probably in reference to its smell. It was an important medicinal herb in the days of Hippocrates, and has had something of a revival in recent decades.

The aroma is irresistible to some animals; cats in particular seem to be almost intoxicated by it, and will roll over and over on the plant. This can destroy a garden plant, and care needs to taken when planting. Rats also seem to like its aroma, and a suggestion is that the Pied Piper of Hamelin owed his success in catching rats to the fact that he carried pieces of Valerian root in his pockets! Strangely enough, in the Middle Ages it was sometimes the custom to lay roots in clothes as a perfume and moth-repellent.

Gerard refers to the traditions of using Valerian for all kinds of ailments, and says that the poorer folk in the north of England and in Scotland used the roots in their broths and pottages to keep themselves healthy. The tenth-century *Leech Book of Bald* describes the uses of Valerian, both internally and also locally for whitlows, swellings, wounds, and so on.

Culpeper describes its actions as "warming and comforting", and recommends it for "difficulty of breathing, coughs, and to expectorate phlegm" among other things. The most significant area of use over the years, however, has been as a relaxant, even sedative, in nervousness, anxiety, neuralgia, insomnia, etc. It was widely used during World War I to calm people who were overwrought with the strain.

## CULTIVATION

Valerian is quite happy in most garden soils, although a rich, moisture-retentive loam is best as it naturally grows near water. Other species are often found in garden centres, but it is *Valeriana officinalis* which must be grown for medicinal uses.

Propagation can be either by dividing the roots, or from seed. Seed germination is both slow and uncertain, so some patience is needed for this method. Do not cover the seeds, as they need the light to germinate. Harvesting of the roots should not be until the second year at least, in the late autumn.

## MODERN MEDICINAL USES

Valerian is one of the most valuable relaxant, anti-spasmodic herbal medicines. The effects are useful both internally for all kinds of tensions and muscle spasms, and locally as a compress for cramps and so on. High over-dosage can cause a heavy, headachy feeling, but in normal circumstances it is calming without being too sedative, and is an excellent non-addictive remedy which herbalists may give to help wean people off tranquillizers.

Additionally, Valerian has expectorant and diuretic properties, which led to some of its traditional applications in bronchial spasm, urinary retention, etc. Whilst not a cure-all, the wide range of uses for Valerian found in the literature demonstrates the value of reducing tension and anxiety in treatment.

Common Vervain from Gerard's *Herball*.

# Vervain

*Verbena officinalis*, Verbenaceae

## DESCRIPTION

Found in the wild in southern and central Europe, as far as the South of England, and also into Asia, Verbena has spread as an escape to many parts of the world. It is often to be found growing by the roadside, or on wasteland.

It is an upright perennial plant with stiff, square stems, forming long, thin branches. The slender leaves are deeply divided and toothed, arranged in pairs. The flowers are rather insignificant, tiny and pale lilac to white in colour, borne on long, slender spikes.

Vervain should not be confused with Lemon Verbena, *Lippia citriodora*, a much larger deciduous shrub with long, highly fragrant, lanceolate leaves. This is of the same genus, and is sometimes called (Lemon) Vervain in France. It has mild digestive and tonic properties, although

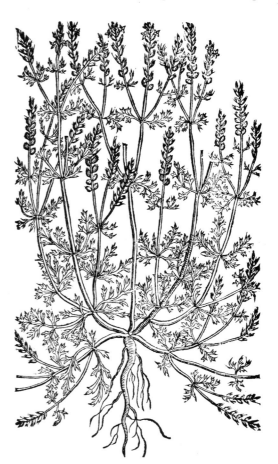

218

*Verbena officinalis*

Published by Dr Woodville. Feb. 1. 1794.

Vervain *Verbena officinalis* from Woodville's *Medical Botany*, 1790.

Messegue felt its actions were in fact stronger than the 'official' Vervain and recommends it for a number of ailments. It makes a delicious lemony tisane, and is often drunk on the Continent.

## HISTORY AND ORIGINS

Vervain has a magical history, and was venerated by the Greeks and Romans as the prime herb for use in sacrifices, burning on the altar and so forth. Old names for it include *Herba Sacra* and Wizard's herb, and the generic name *Verbena* was used by the Romans to signify an altar-herb.

Magicians and sorcerers of all cultures regarded it as a favourite, and there are many legends attached to it. Vervain was one of the three most sacred herbs of the Druids, who employed it in various healing rites. They believed it could heal all wounds made in battle, and this idea is echoed in the legend that it was found growing on Calvary and was used to staunch the wounds of the crucifixion.

Alongside these magical qualities, Vervain was thought to be a virtual panacea for kidney, liver and heart disorders, as well as fevers, difficulties in labour and more. It was also used in classical times as an aphrodisiac, sometimes being called the herb of Venus!

By the Middle Ages, the mystical notions had receded in most of the herbals, although not in folk-lore, and the therapeutic indications were for more physical complaints. In the sixteenth century Matthiolus could still write: "Sorcerers lose their senses at the mention of this herb," but herbalists were more concerned with its value in tertian and quartan agues, or fevers.

Gerard is very down to earth in these matters, as befits a gardener, and says: "Many odde old wives fables are written of Vervaine tending to witchcraft and sorcery, which you may reade elsewhere, for I am not willing to trouble your eares with reporting such trifles." Culpeper recommends Vervain in disorders of the digestive system, jaundice and also in urinary stones, as well as in some fevers.

Possibly due to the decline in magic and mysticism during the last two hundred years or so, the value placed on Vervain medicinally also declined. However, in this century it has become an increasingly useful remedy in certain conditions.

## CULTIVATION

Vervain grows easily from seed, sown in early spring. As it is a perennial it can be propagated by division of the roots. It generally prefers a sunny position, and a reasonably well-drained soil, but as a common wild plant it is able to survive quite well in many situations.

Lemon Verbena is incidentally rather a

tender plant, and it needs some protection from frosts in this country. It originated in Chile, and prefers a dry, quite poor soil.

## MODERN MEDICINAL USES

Vervain is a valuable tonic in exhaustion, convalescence and other conditions of debility. It has some diaphoretic properties, inducing sweating in feverish conditions such as influenza. It exerts an anti-spasmodic effect on the internal organs, and may be prescribed in instances of excess tension, such as migraines, period cramps, asthma etc.

As a digestive and liver tonic, Vervain has a useful role in the treatment of problems like glandular fever and weak digestion. It is a galactogogue, stimulating milk production in breast-feeding mothers. Finally, it can be helpful as a mouthwash/gargle in sore throats, inflamed gums and so on.

# Sweet Violet

*Viola odorata*, Violaceae

## DESCRIPTION

There are a great number of species of Violet spread around the world, forming trees in tropical climates, but seen only as flowering plants in temperate zones. *Viola odorata* is sometimes called English Violet, and is a native of this country. It is found in places through Europe, and has been cultivated in America and elsewhere.

It is a small perennial herb, growing in

Sweet Violet *Viola odorata* from *Flora Londinensis*, W. Curtis 1777.

*Viola odorata.*

banks, hedgerows and woodland borders, and is easy to miss. It has a thick, creeping rhizome, from which rise the heart-shaped leaves, initially curled up into two coils. They emerge as early as late February, and open into a rosette. From this rise the flowering stalks.

The flowers are usually a delicate shade of purple, giving their name to the colour violet, but there is a variety, *Viola odorata* 'Alba' which produces white flowers with a faint tinge of violet. They have five petals, the central lower one slightly elongated into a spur shape underneath. The flowers are sweet-scented, and attractive to bees, but normally have finished flowering by late April before pollination can take place. The plants produce much smaller flowers in the autumn, which produce the seed.

## HISTORY AND ORIGINS

Violets are probably the most written-about herbs in the world, and featured regularly in the works of Virgil and Homer. The Greeks loved the plant so much that they made it the emblem of Athens, and there are records of it being grown commercially and sent to Athens market in 400 BC. The origin of its name is obscure; the most romantic version is that it was named after Io, whom Zeus turned into a cow in order for her to escape the jealous wrath of Hera. The god created the plant for the animal to browse on.

Both Greeks and Romans used the Violet extensively in medicine and perfumery. They drank violet-flavoured wine to calm and relax and 'comfort the heart'. Hippocrates recommended it for headaches, depression and bronchial inflammation. In the first century BC, Horace wrote a complaint that Roman gardeners spent more time on their Violet beds than on tending the olive groves!

Shakespeare, like countless others before and since, delighted in the Violet, which grew abundantly around Stratford-upon-Avon.

Keats called it "that queen of secrecy", and the French herbalist Messegue describes how his father made his own perfume from it. In the Victorian era, it was immensely popular and bunches were worn by everybody. Queen Victoria visited the famous herb-growing area of Grasse, in France, and declared their Violet perfumes exquisite.

The flowers have been crystallized as a sweet, and back in the days of Charles II a popular conserve was Violet Plate, or sugar, given to consumptives and sold everywhere. The fresh flowers have also been used in salads.

As a medicine, Sweet Violet has had many traditional uses. Gerard declares that the flowers "are good for all inflammations, especially of the sides and lungs", and Culpeper recommends them externally for inflamed swellings as well as internally to reduce pain and inflammation. The flowers are gently laxative, and a syrup was formerly an official medicine for childhood constipation. One of the most interesting areas of use has been in cancer, and this is an aspect where it is of some value today.

## CULTIVATION

Violets have been developed over the centuries by cultivation to the point where there are hundreds of garden varieties. To grow the wild Sweet Violet, an unpolluted atmosphere is almost a necessity, since they are badly affected by dirt, fumes and grime.

The Sweet Violet prefers at least partial shade, certainly in the height of summer. It is best grown in a medium-rich soil, not too heavy. Propagation is by rooted runners; these need replenishment virtually every year in order to avoid overcrowding and consequently having plants with lots of leaf but no flowers.

## MODERN MEDICINAL USES

Sweet Violet has considerable value in modern herbal medicine. The pain-relieving and anti-inflammatory properties noted by the old writers are largely due to its content of methyl salicylate, a compound similar to aspirin. It is also a stimulating expectorant, and has a useful role to play in the treatment of bronchitis and other chest infections.

There is some evidence for an action against tumours, and it may be prescribed as a background remedy in some kinds of cancerous conditions.

# Witch Hazel

*Hamamelis virginiana*, Hamamelidaceae

## DESCRIPTION

Witch Hazel is a small, deciduous tree that is indigenous to woodlands on the eastern side of America and Canada, but is found in cultivation in gardens in many countries.

The tree grows to some fifteen feet or so, with a smooth, grey-brown bark and crooked branches. The large, ovate leaves are arranged alternately on the branches; they have prominent veins and indented margins. In the autumn, the leaves drop off and in late autumn to early winter the flowers appear. They are a pale yellow, and hang in drooping clusters. These are followed by small, black nuts which in mild climates produce seeds by the following summer.

There are many varieties of Witch Hazel which make good ornamental trees, to bring some winter colour to the garden, and also a light fragrance from the flowers.

## HISTORY AND ORIGINS

Witch Hazel is widely available in its distilled form, and recognized as a first-aid remedy for all kinds of bruises, swellings, etc. It was traditionally highly valued by the North American Indians for these same purposes, and they had employed the leaves and bark externally for centuries, for inflamed skin disorders.

The leaves quickly became an official remedy in the *US Pharmacopoeia*. Both they and the bark contain gallic acid, as well as other tannins, and the astringent action was appreciated by herbalists and orthodox physicians alike. In Victorian times there was a famous preparation called 'Pond's Extract of Witch Hazel', as a domestic remedy for all manner of knocks, burns, etc., and the distilled liquid today is a successor to this. It is the prime ingredient in most commercial eyewashes.

## CULTIVATION

Witch Hazel is quite slow-growing, and it is advisable to purchase a large specimen in order to get a decent-sized tree within a few years. It naturally grows in a dampish situation, and the usual precautions regarding proper preparation of the hole for planting trees should be observed. The leaves can be collected to make an infusion for applying to the skin.

## MODERN MEDICINAL USES

Herbalists use a tincture of Witch Hazel that contains the tannins in full, unlike the commercial distilled variety, and so they often get a much stronger action.

It is one of the major external remedies for all kinds of swelling and inflammation; it can be used as a cold compress for bruises, sprains, wounds, insect bites and other first-aid problems. An ointment is excellent for use on haemorrhoids, and a compress can be used on varicose veins to great effect.

Internally, Witch Hazel is both astringent and anti-inflammatory, and may be used in the treatment of diarrhoea, enteritis and even internal bleeding, including bowel disorders and haemorrhoids. Wherever an astringent is required, Witch Hazel may be thought of for local and internal medication.

# Yarrow

*Achillea millefolium*, Compositae

## DESCRIPTION

Yarrow is an extremely widespread plant, found on roadsides, hedgerows, waste ground and in meadows throughout the world. It is a perennial, creeping herb that grows to about two feet. It spreads both by the roots and by prolific seeding, and is often thought of as a troublesome nuisance by gardeners and farmers.

The tough, angular stems carry the very finely divided leaves that give the plant its Latin name of 'thousand-leaf', and create an almost feathery appearance. The flowers appear through the

Witch Hazel *Hamamelis virginiana* from *Curtis's Botanical Magazine*, 1882.

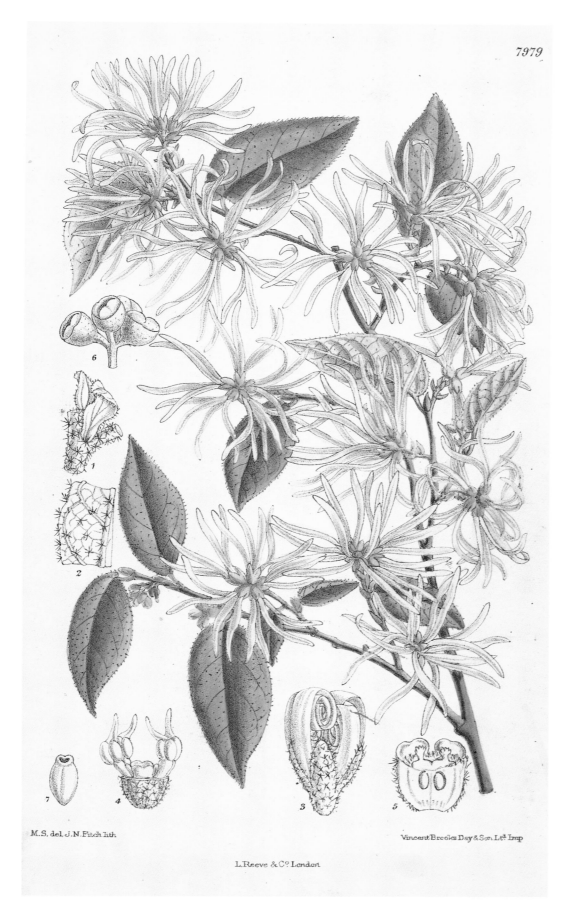

summer, and are arranged in flattened, dense terminal heads. They are white, sometimes verging on pink, with a slight but distinctive aroma.

## HISTORY AND ORIGINS

Yarrow is famous as the herb that supposedly staunched the wound that Achilles suffered during the siege of Troy, on the recommendation of the goddess Aphrodite, hence its generic name. Other versions say its actions were discovered by another Achilles, disciple of the legendary centaur Chiron. Since Greek times it has been used as a wound herb, to stop bleeding, and many nicknames testify to this reputation.

It was also called Nosebleed, and the finely divided leaves were stuffed into the nostrils to staunch the flow of blood in this condition. The seventeenth-century herbalist Parkinson wrote that "if it be put into the nose, assuredly it will stay the

Common Yarrow from Gerard's *Herball*.

Witch Hazel *Hamamelis virginiana* from *Curtis's Botanical Magazine*, 1904.

1. *Achillea millefolium*___2. *Achillea tomentosa*___3. *Achillea Clarenæ*.
4. *Marshallia cæspitosa*.

Day & Haghe, Lith.rs to the Queen.

64

*Achillea Millefolium.*

Published by Dr Woodville Jan.1 1, 1791.

Yarrow *Achillea millfolium* from Woodville's *Medical Botany*, 1790.

Opposite: Yarrow from Mrs Loudon's *The Ladies' Flower-Garden of Ornamental Perennials Vol. II*, 1843–44. 1. *Achillea milfolium* 2. *A. tomentosa* 3. *A. clavennae* 4. *Marshallia caespitosa*.

Yarrow in his suggestions for use, calling it "drying and binding".

Yarrow was much used in Scandinavia to make ale, and was drunk as a remedy for rheumatic complaints. Infusions of Yarrow are a traditional remedy in feverish colds and 'flu, and it has established a reputation for improving menstrual blood flow and circulation generally.

## CULTIVATION

Yarrow is easy to grow, and harder to eradicate once established! It likes a dryish, sunny spot. Collecting the plant from the wild may be an option for people wishing to make an infusion, say for a cold, and not wanting to grow it. There are many ornamental members of the Achillea family which can be cultivated, but they lack Yarrow's medicinal properties.

## MODERN MEDICINAL USES

Yarrow is an important medicinal plant; not only does it have benefits as a vulnerary, or wound herb, but more usefully today it is recognized as an excellent digestive tonic, vasodilator and diaphoretic as well as a regulator of menstruation.

Hot infusions of Yarrow induce sweating, and are diuretic, and help a lot in feverish ailments. This action is supported by its ability to encourage the distribution of the circulation to the extremities by dilating the blood-vessels. In some instances of hypertension this means that Yarrow is a very beneficial remedy, and poor circulation, chilblains, etc., can be treated by herbalists with this plant amongst others.

It aids digestion and restores lost appetite, for example in convalescence. It is helpful in cases of excessive menstrual bleeding, or blood loss from haemorrhoids, leading to anaemia. The diuretic effect can be effective in treating mild cases of cystitis. Doctors on the continent who use phytotherapy, or herbal medicine, rate Yarrow very highly in general practice, and prescribe it as a tonic in chronic debility.

bleeding of it". On the other hand, it has been taken as a snuff, to induce sneezing and bleeding and so lessen nasal congestion and/or headaches, so it would seem to have gained this name both ways!

The ancient military uses as a wound herb had a more recent echo, when soldiers in World War I employed Yarrow to dress wounds when they had no other dressings available. Culpeper emphasizes the astringent properties of

Pl. 40.

*Aconitum Napellus.*

W.H. Lizars sculpt

# CHAPTER V

# Poisonous Plants

## Aconite

*Aconitum napellus*, Ranunculaceae

### DESCRIPTION

Aconite is a native of mountain meadows in central Europe, stretching across to the lower slopes of the Himalayas. It was introduced into Britain at an early date, and is found as an escape here and elsewhere.

It is a hardy perennial, growing to three feet or more, with handsome flower spikes of blue, helmet-shaped flowers. Their appearance gives rise to some of its other names, such as Monkshood. The leaves are a dark, shiny green, deeply divided into a palmate shape.

The roots are rather tuberous; each spring as the bud that will produce the flowering stem starts to shoot, lateral buds send down roots. These absorb matter from the parent root, which slowly dies away. By the autumn the new roots are full of starch, ready for the process to begin again the next year.

### HISTORY AND ORIGINS

Aconite is one of the most poisonous herbs, a fact which was appreciated by early writers. A nickname for it is Wolf's Bane, a reference to the idea that arrows tipped with its juice were useful to kill

Opposite: Aconite, Common Monkshood or Wolfsbane *Aconitum napellus* from *Hortus Medicus* by George Graves, 1834.

Monkshood from *Commentarii in Sex Libros Pedacii Dioscoridis* by Pierandrea Matthioli, 1565.

wolves. The generic name derives from the Greek word *akontion*, a dart, for similar reasons.

The deadly nature of Aconite was said in legend to have been created by Hecate, from the foam from the mouth of the gigantic dog that guarded hell, Cerberus. It was used to give as a drink to old men in Greek times when they were no longer of use to the state, and crops up in a number of myths. Its actions on the heart, combined with Belladonna, or Henbane, created the delirious hallucinations of medieval witches' flying ointments.

Gerard says: "The force and faculties of Wolfs-bane is deadly to man and all kindes of beasts", and describes instances of people accidentally taking the plant, and dying. Like others, he thought more poisonous than at all useful, although it had some reputation as an antidote to other poisons. This may well have been more fancy than fact, especially as Gerard suggests simply throwing the herb in front of a scorpion in order to paralyse it and stop it stinging!

By Culpeper's day, even these uses were declining. He describes a related alpine species, which he terms 'Wholesome Aconite', as an antidote against vegetable poisons (with no modern justification), but says "it is not much regarded at this time".

During the last century, Aconite was valued much more highly as a medicine, both locally as a liniment to lessen the pains of sciatica, lumbago and so on, and internally for fevers or cardiac failure. It was listed in the *British Pharmacopoeia*, but was also restricted as a scheduled poison.

## CULTIVATION

Aconite likes a moist soil, and a fairly rich loam suits it quite well. It prefers partial shade and grows taller in places such as open woodland, or on the edges of upland meadows bordering on trees. Traditionally, it was collected from the Tyrol and Switzerland. There are many kinds of Aconite, and they carry similarly toxic alkaloids, but *Aconitum napellus* is the herb specified.

## MODERN MEDICINAL USES

Aconite is so poisonous that an internal dose that might be effective in medicine is almost identical to a toxic one. The content of the deadly alkaloid, Aconitine, varies between plants to a considerable extent, which further makes it hazardous. Accordingly, it is *never* to be used internally, and in the rare circumstances that it is professionally prescribed for external use, it should not be applied over broken skin.

The dosage of the lotion is strictly controlled by law; it has a strong effect in reducing the pains of neuralgia, sciatica and the like. The herb is a significant remedy in homoeopathic medicine, where dosage is of course minute.

# Black Hellebore

*Helleborus niger*, Ranunculaceae

## DESCRIPTION

Black Hellebore is a native of the mountains of southern Europe and Asia Minor, but is cultivated in gardens in Britain and elsewhere. It is more commonly known to gardeners as the Christmas Rose, since it comes into flower at this time.

Hellebore is a perennial, with dark-coloured roots that give it the name Black Hellebore, although they are whitish inside. The shiny green leaves are divided into five or more segments, and stay green all wiinter. The white flowers bloom in late winter, mostly single on flower-stalks that rise directly from the rootstock; they gradually fade to a dull pink.

Black Hellebore should not be confused with others, such as Bearsfoot, *Helleborus foetidus*, the Green Hellebore, *Helleborus viridis* or *Veratrum viride*, or White Hellebore, *Veratrum album*, or even the False Hellebore, *Adonis vernalis*, *usually called Pheasant's Eye. All these plants are highly poisonous.*

## HISTORY AND ORIGINS

In old times, Hellebore was known as *Melampodium*, after a Greek physician called Melampos. He is credited with using it to cure mania and madness, about 1400 BC, and the name appears in herbals as late as Gerard. The latter describes how Hellebore was used to treat animals such as cows and horses when they had bad coughs or wheezing, by cutting a slit in the loose skin under the throat and inserting a piece of Hellebore root. After a few days, the root was removed; this process was known as 'Settering' the animal, and an old name for Hellebore is Setter-wort.

The chief action of Hellebore is as a drastic purgative, and this was considered valuable in removing the black bile, so improving melancholia. These lines are from Burton's *Anatomy of Melancholy*:

Borage and Hellebore fill two scenes,
Sovereign plants to purge the veins
Of melancholy, and cheer the heart
Of those black fumes which make it smart.

Gerard gives the virtues of Black Hellebore as a purge "for mad and furious men, for melancholy, dull and heavie persons, and briefly for all those that are troubled with black choler, and molested with melancholy".

Culpeper advised its use with caution, to bring on periods and as a purge. He mentions that goat's milk is an antidote for it, although there is no modern proof of this! An interesting use he suggests is using the powdered root externally on ulcers and gangrenous wounds.

## CULTIVATION

Hellebore do well in ordinary garden soil. They prefer a sheltered position, with partial shade and good drainage. They can be propagated by seed, pricked out into a shady border and finally transplanted in the following year, or else by division of the roots from established plants.

## MODERN MEDICINAL USES

Black Hellebore is a violent purgative and emmenagogue, provoking menstruation;

Opposite: Black Hellebore or Christmas Rose *Helleborus niger* from Woodville's *Medical Botany*, 1790.

*Helleborus niger.*

Published by Dr. Woodville April 1. 1790.

Hellebores from Mrs Loudon's *The Ladies' Flower-Garden of Ornamental Perennials* Vol I, 1843–44. 1. *Helleborus niger* 2. *H. lividus* 3. *H. odorus* 4. *Trollius americanus* 5. *T. europaeus* 6. *Isopyrum grandiflorum* 7. *Coptis trifolia* 8. *Eranthus hyemalis*.

it has strong narcotic properties as well. The highly poisonous nature of this plant means that it, like the other Hellebores, are not used in herbal medicine at all now.

# Hemlock

*Conium maculatum*, Umbelliferae

## Description

Hemlock is found wild in meadows and by river banks throughout most of Europe, including Britain, and parts of Asia; it was introduced into America, and grows in similar places there.

Hemlock is a member of the parsnip and carrot family, and there have been occasional fatal mistakes when people have eaten parts of the plant instead of other edible species.

It is a tall, rather stately plant with the typically finely divided foliage of its family. It can be distinguished by the smooth, shiny stems, which are spotted with red blotches. It is a biennial, growing to around four feet, or more in sheltered sites.

The umbels of white flowers are followed by small fruit, very similar to caraway in appearance. If the plant is bruised it gives an unpleasant odour, hich is another means of identification. The seeds have a bitter taste. All parts are poisonous.

## History and Origins

The poisonous qualities of Hemlock were very well known to the Ancient Greeks, and it is perhaps most famous as the fatal juice which Socrates was condemned to drink. It has powerfully sedative and narcotic effects, and the generic name is derived from a Greek word meaning 'to whirl about'.

An old story gave the origins of the dark red blotches on the stems as representing the marks on Cain's brow after he had slain Abel. It was employed in early medicine as an external remedy for scrofulous swellings, tumours and so on, and is described in this respect in this country as early as the tenth century by the Anglo-Saxon physicians.

Culpeper refers to these uses, saying it may be applied "to inflammations, tumults, and swellings in any part of the body, as also St Anthony's fire, wheals, pushes, and creeping ulcers that arise of hot, sharp tumours". This is a graphic account of the kinds of ailments that people suffered from in his day; his works, like those of other medieval herbalists, are littered with suggestions for applications for all sorts of gangrenous wounds, ulcers, etc.

The use of Hemlock declined after his day, but was revived in the eighteenth

Opposite: Hemlock *Conium maculatum* from *Hortus Medicus* by George Graves, 1834.

Pl. 37.

*1*     *2*     *3*

*Conium maculatum.*

W.H.Lizars sculp.t

Hemlock from Gerard's *Herball*.

century by Dr Storch, or Stoerk as some writers called him, of Vienna. He primarily advised it for external treatment of cancerous and other ulcers. It was occasionally used as a substitute for opium internally, with similar overdosage effects. One distinctive effect of fatal poisoning with Hemlock is the thinning of the blood, one surgeon reporting in the nineteenth century that, "on opening the head a quantity flowed out, which twice filled an ordinary chamber-pot"!

It has been infrequently used as an antidote for strychnine poisoning, and in medieval times was considered a remedy for hydrophobia, from the bite of a mad dog. It is itself partly antidoted by caffeine or similar stimulants.

## CULTIVATION

Hemlock grows as a wayside weed quite easily, and its toxicity to humans and animals are sufficient reason not to grow it in the garden at all.

## MODERN MEDICINAL USES

Hemlock paralyses the motor centres of the nervous system, and poisoning results in respiratory depression, loss of speech, comatose sleep and eventually death. If awake, the mind remains unaffected to the end. It is on the Schedule of Poisons, and is not used at all in modern times. The external applications may be worth scientific research, but it should be avoided by non-medically qualified people.

# Henbane

*Hyoscyamus niger*, Solanaceae

## DESCRIPTION

Henbane is a native of southern Europe and Asia, found as far as India, but is also found on waste ground in Britain. There is a record of 1672 which refers to it growing in America, "sprung up since the English planted and kept cattle in New England".

It is a member of the potato family, which contains several highly poisonous species such as Deadly Nightshade. It can be variable in size and appearance, normally living as a biennial but sometimes only surviving annually. The large, irregularly divided leaves are coarse and hairy. In its biennial form it can grow to three feet, but is much smaller as an annual.

The dull yellow, pitcher-shaped flowers generally have purplish vein markings on them, and are carried on the flowering stems which rise from a basal rosette of leaves. The stems also carry leaves, arranged alternately up the hairy stem, and it is these which have been used medicinally. The whole plant has a nauseating odour, and is poisonous.

## HISTORY AND ORIGINS

A medicinal plant from ancient times, Henbane was recommended by Dioscorides as an analgesic and to promote sleep. His advice was echoed by others through until the Middle Ages. Gerard says Henbane "causeth drowsinesse, and

mitigateth all kinde of paine", but he recognizes the potential dangers, saying it can easily cause "an unquiet sleep like unto the sleepe of drunkennesse, which continueth long, and is deadly to the party".

References to Henbane appear in many works; for example, Shakespeare has Hamlet's father describing how:

Upon my secure hour thy uncle stole,
With juice of cursed hebenon in a vial,
And in the porches of mine ear did pour
The leprous distillment.

(There is some argument whether this term, common in Elizabethan times, referred to Henbane or is a corrupt version of the Yew.)

Henbane is placed by Culpeper "under the dominion of Saturn", which in his astrological terminology indicated its toxic nature, like Hemlock and so on. He

Opposite: Common Henbane *Hyosciamus niger* from *Hortus Medicus* by George Graves, 1834.

Henbane from Gerard's *Herball*.

*Hyosciamus niger.*

L. *Helleborus niger.*
I. *Elleboro nero.*
G. *Viraire noir.*
Ge. *Christwurtz. oste*
*Swart Niescruyt.*

Black Hellebore from *Hortus Floridus* by Crispin de Pass, 1614.

ascribes great healing powers to it locally for inflammation and swellings, and says it should not be used internally, "it is altogether an outward medicine", even for headaches and sleeplessness.

The capacity of Henbane to induce stupor, giddiness and delirium led to its use in magical rites, and it was an ingredient in medieval 'flying ointments' of witches, who experienced hallucinations of flying through the air to gatherings. In mythology, it was supposed to be given to the dead as a crown as they wandered by the river Styx in the underworld.

## Cultivation

In Mrs Grieve's day the plant was in such demand medicinally that the wild plants were not enough to satisfy the pharmacies, and it was cultivated widely in Britain and Europe. Henbane will grow on most soils, but it is difficult to get the seeds to germinate well. Sometimes they will lie dormant for a year or two.

It requires a moderately fertile soil, well-drained and in a sunny position. The seed is very small, and has often been mixed with sand to sow it. Its poisonous nature is a good reason not to grow it, although its nauseous smell and taste have meant that there were few cases of poisoning by accidental intake.

## Modern Medicinal Uses

Henbane is a powerful anti-spasmodic, and narcotic sedative. It owes most of its former action to the alkaloid hyoscyamine, whilst the analgesic, narcotic effects are largely due to another alkaloid, hyoscine, or scopolamine — famed in spy stories as the 'truth drug'.

Supply and dosage are strictly confined to professional medical herbalists, who rarely use it in any case. Low doses are effective in reducing the spasms of asthma or severe colic, but its toxicity means extreme caution is needed.

## Deadly Nightshade

*Atropa belladonna*, Solanaceae

### Description

Deadly Nightshade, or Belladonna, is found widely through southern Europe and western Asia, and has long been cultivated in Britain and America. It is

Opposite: Woody Nightshade *Solanum dulcamara* from *Hortus Medicus* by George Graves, 1834.

136

Pl.8.

Pl.7.

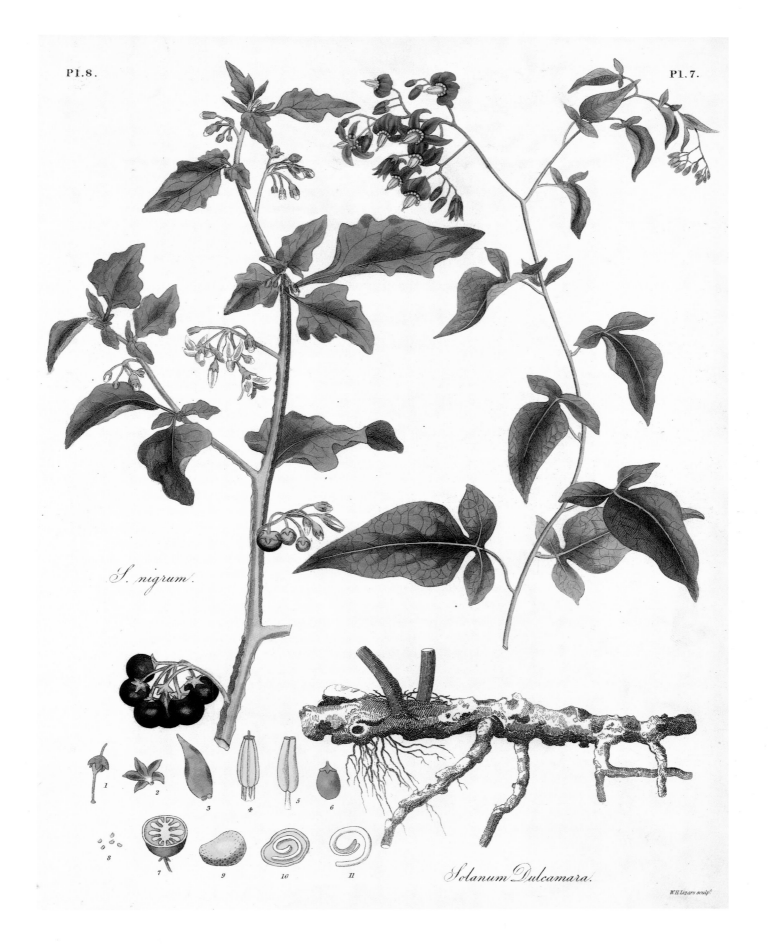

*S. nigrum.*

*Solanum Dulcamara.*

*W.H.Lizars sculp.*

Pl. 6.

*Atropa Belladonna.*

now scarcer in this country, due to the decline in cultivation for medicinal purposes and worries over children eating the poisonous berries.

The perennial roots are thick and fleshy, of a whitish colour. The stems rise up each year to some three or four feet; they are purplish, branching and carry many ovate leaves. These are a dull, dark green and come in two different sizes, arranged in pairs, one large and one small, alternately up the stems. The veins on the underside are quite prominent.

The solitary flowers bloom from early summer to September. They are large, bell-shaped and a dull, purplish-green colour, growing on short stalks in the leaf axils. The fruit that succeeds the flowers are large, almost cherry-sized and a shiny, black colour. They are juicy and quite sweet to taste, hence the danger to children.

### HISTORY AND ORIGINS

The names of this plant give useful clues to its effects and traditional experiences. Belladonna, literally 'beautiful lady', is believed to be a reference to the habit of Italian ladies in medieval times of dropping the juice into their eyes to make the pupils dilate and so increase their attractiveness. The chief ingredient that induces this effect, atropine, is widely used in ophthalmology to this day as the finest dilator of the pupils, in minute doses.

The word *Atropa* is derived from the Greek Atropos, who was one of the Fates and held the shears to cut the thread of life — a strong hint of its potentially deadly nature, echoed in the common name. From the time of Chaucer, the plant was known in this country as Dwale, probably from a word meaning 'to sleep'. Gerard calls it Sleepy Night-

Deadly Nightshade from Gerard's *Herball*.

shade, and says: "This kind of Nightshade causeth sleep, troubleth the mind, bringeth madnesse if a few of the berries be inwardly taken."

A related species, *Atropa mandragora*, was used as far back as Roman times as an anaesthetic. It is believed to be the wine that Circe gave to Odysseus' companions, and also the sleeping draught that was given to Juliet.

Despite its poisonous effects on humans, some animals and birds can eat the leaves and berries with no problems at all. Cats and dogs, however, are easily poisoned by it.

Given all this it might be wondered why it was used at all. The powerfully relaxant and central nervous depressant actions have been used as a very powerful anti-spasmodic, in conditions like asthma, colic, cardiac pains and enuresis. Equally, it has a long tradition in external applications. Culpeper, for instance, says: "It is not good at all for inward uses; but both leaves and root may with good success be applied outwardly, by way of poultice, to inflammatory swellings."

### CULTIVATION

Much work was done in earlier years to determine what conditions gave the maximum alkaloid content. Deadly Nightshade seems to prefer a light, chalky soil, with a south-west aspect being ideal; some shade will ensure the plant grows taller and is less bothered by pests. It grows wild on stony ground, and good drainage is essential.

Due to its toxicity, Belladonna should not be grown in gardens where young children play, and care should be taken to wear gloves when pruning or handling the plant, since the juice can be taken into a cut or abrasion.

### MODERN MEDICINAL USES

Deadly Nightshade owes most of its effects to the powerful alkaloids atropine and hyoscyamine, and their toxicity means that it is scarcely used. It is only available to professional practitioners anyway, and dosage is strictly controlled by law. The lowest doses possible would be used on the rare occasions that it might be prescribed. On the Continent, it is highly regarded by doctors practising phytotherapy, in specific circumstances. It is an important remedy in homoeopathic medicine, where the doses are infinitesimally small in any case.

Opposite: Deadly Nightshade *Atropa belladonna* from *Hortus Medicus* by George Graves, 1834.

1. *Aconitum heterophyllum*.— 2. *Aconitum Anthora*.— 3. *Aconitum ochroleucum*.— 4. *Aconitum Australe*.
5. *Aconitum paniculatum*.— 6. *Aconitum versicolor*.— 7. *Aconitum napellus*.— 8. *Aconitum variegatum*.

Day & Haghe Lith.rs to the Queen

# Index

# BIBLIOGRAPHY

Bown, D. *Fine Herbs*, London, Unwin Hyman (1988)

Culpeper, N. *English Physician* (1651)

Evans, M. *A Guide to Herbal Remedies*, Saffron Waldon, C. W. Daniel (1990)

Gerard, J. *Herball* (1597)

Graves, G. *Hortus Medicus* (1834)

Grieve, M. *A Modern Herbal*, London, Jonathan Cape (1931)

Griggs, B. *Green Pharmacy*, London, Jill, Norman & Hobhouse (1981)

Hoffman, D. *The Holistic Herbal*, Forres, Findhorn Press (1983)

Hoffman, D. *Welsh Herbal Medicine*, Abercastle, Abercastle Publications (1978)

Keys, J. *Chinese Herbs*, Tokyo, Charles E. Tuttle (1976)

Lowenfeld, C. *Herb Gardening*, London, Faber & Faber (1964)

Messegue, M. *Health Secrets of Plants and Herbs*, London, Collins (1979)

Mills, S. *The Dictionary of Modern Herbalism*, Wellingborough, Thorsons (1985)

Palaiseul, J. *Grandmother's Secrets*, Harmondsworth, Penguin (1976)

Phillips, R. *Wild Flowers of Britain*, London, Pan (1977)

Weiss, R. *Herbal Medicine*, Beaconsfield, Beaconsfield Publishers (1988)

# ACKNOWLEDGEMENTS

The publishers would like to thank the following for their help in the compilation of this book:
The Linnean Society of London: the Council and Librarian, Gina Douglas; Paul Quarrie, Eton College Librarian and Keeper of the College Collections; Sarah Hollis and Michael Carter.

The publishers would like to thank the following for their permission to reproduce the original prints in their possession: British Library, London, jacket image and page 15 (BL MS 19720 f165); Her Majesty The Queen for the illustration on the title-page, © Windsor Castle, Royal Library; Scala Florence for 'The Thebaidi Monks' by Lorenzetti (Uffizi), and the detail of this painting, on page 13. The Linnean Society of London for the illustrations on pages 10, 14, 24, 41, 44, 48, 50, 59, 60, 61, 67, 69, 70, 81, 86, 87, 89, 96, 96, 99, 109, 110 and 122; The Provost and Fellows of Eton College for the illustrations on pages 20, 23, 24, 34, 112 and 140; The Bodleian Library, University of Oxford for the following illustrations, pages 25 and 26 (L.1.5.Med), page 69 (MS Ashmole 1504, fol.15v), page 93 (MS Ashmole 1504, fol.12) and page 111 (MS Ashmole 1504, fol.16); The British Museum (Natural History), London for the illustrations on pages 28 and 37; The Glasgow Museum and Art Gallery, Kelvingrove for the illustration on page 84. Wheldon and Wesley Limited for the pictures on pages 124 and 125.